CONCEPTS IN CHEMISTRY

An
Introduction
To Chemical
Energetics

CONCEPTS IN CHEMISTRY

An Introduction To Chemical Energetics

J. J. THOMPSON

UNIVERSITY OF SUSSEX

HOUGHTON MIFFLIN COMPANY · BOSTON
New York Atlanta Geneva, Illinois Dallas Palo Alto

First published in Great Britain by Longmans, Green and Co., Ltd.

First published in the U.S.A. by Houghton Mifflin Company

PRINTED IN THE U.S.A.

Preface

This monograph has as its aim the introduction of such topics as free energy and entropy at a fairly elementary level.

The approach adopted is essentially non-mathematical so far as is possible with a subject of this nature, and it is hoped that this will prove useful to those chemistry students without background in advanced mathematics. Therefore the treatment is intentionally not rigorous, nor is it traditional in the sense that no reference is made to the Carnot cycle for example, but each concept is introduced through a consideration of systems which are within the range of experience of every freshman student.

It is hoped that the sections concerned with the practical measurements of the several kinds of energy change will be especially useful, and that through such experiments the student will be brought to a clearer understanding of these difficult topics.

I would like to thank the Oxford and Cambridge Examinations Board for permission to reproduce material from questions set in their examinations. I am also grateful to M. G. Brown of the University of Sussex, and to T. A. G. Silk of Blundell's School, who read the manuscript, and to my colleague G. R. Walker who read the proofs, all of whom had many helpful comments and criticisms to make.

J. J. Thompson

Contents

Preface   v

Part One *Introduction*

1 *The Driving Force for Chemical Reaction*   3
  Spontaneous reaction   3
  Energy changes in spontaneous processes   4
  Entropy changes in spontaneous processes   7
  Types of systems   9
  The stretching of rubber   9
  Dissolution of ammonium nitrate   10
  Free energy changes   10

Part Two *Heat Changes in Chemical Reactions*

2 *Definitions, Conventions and Laws*   15
  Sign of the heat change   15
  Units in which heat changes are measured   15
  Standard heat changes   15
  Some special heats of reaction   16
  Heats of formation   16
  Heats of combustion   17
  Heats of dissociation   18
  Heats of neutralisation   18
  Heat of solution   19
  Laws of thermochemistry   19
  Effect of external conditions on the heat change   22
  The effect of temperature on heat changes   24
  Heat capacity   24
  Kirchhoff's equation   25

3 *The Measurement of Heat Changes*   29
  The measurement of temperature changes   29
  The reaction vessel   29
  Determination of the calorimeter constant   31
  Practical exercises (1–5) for the students   32

4 *Sources of Heat Changes*   39
  Kinetic energy of a substance   39
  Potential energy of a substance   40
  A. IONIC BONDS   40
  Lattice energy   40
  The solubility of ionic compounds   44
  B. COVALENT BONDS   45

Nature of the bond   45
Bond energy   46
Zero-point energy   48
Constancy of bond energy   49
Factors affecting the magnitude of the bond energy   51
C. COORDINATE BONDS   55
D. METALLIC BONDS   56
E. HYDROGEN BONDS   57
F. OTHER TYPES OF BOND   58

Part Three *Entropy Changes in Chemical Reactions*

5 *Sources of Entropy Changes*   61
Entropy and probability   •   61
Reactions in which there is a change of state   61
Reactions in which simple species are produced from   65
    more complex ones, and vice versa
Effect of mass on the entropy of gases   67

6 *Entropy as a Thermodynamic Function*   69
Thermodynamics and thermodynamic functions   69
Extensive and intensive properties   69
Reversible and irreversible processes   69
Concept of entropy   70
Units of entropy   71
Second Law of Thermodynamics   71
Entropy changes for an ideal gas   71
Entropy changes for changes in state   72
Entropy changes for real substances   74
Absolute entropy values   74
Evidence for the Third Law   76
Exceptions to the Third Law   76

7 *The Measurement of Entropy Changes*   78
Entropy of vaporisation and fusion   78
Entropy of transition between allotropic forms   78
Entropy measurements from cell reactions   79
Practical exercises (6 and 7) for the students   80

Part Four *Free Energy Changes in Chemical Reactions*

8 *Free Energy as a Thermodynamic Function*   85
Free energy and net work   85
Standard free energy changes   87
The effect of temperature on the free energy change   89

9   *Free Energy and Equilibrium*   94
    Reversible reactions   94
    Free energy and the equilibrium constant   95
    The equilibrium constant   96
    Use of the isotherm   96
    Variation of equilibrium constant with temperature   98
    Le Chatelier's Principle   99

10 *Summary of the Main Principles*   100
    (1) Direction of spontaneous reaction   100
    (2) Position of equilibrium   101
    (3) Useful work obtainable from a reaction   101
    (4) Determination of the stability of a substance   102

    Further Reading   104

    Index   105

Part One
Introduction

1 The Driving Force for Chemical Reaction

Of all the questions which are asked by chemistry students probably the most fundamental is 'Why do chemical reactions take place? Why, when one substance is placed in contact with another will chemical change occur, when other pairs of substances will not react together under similar conditions?' We are really asking ourselves 'What is the *driving force* of a chemical reaction?', and the purpose of this monograph is to attempt to find an answer to this question. Briefly, we shall examine the factors which affect the nature of chemical change for many processes and reactions which are known to 'work', and thus arrive at some criterion by which we may establish whether a proposed reaction will take place or not.

Spontaneous reaction

It is essential that before we begin to look for an answer to our question we understand exactly what we mean by chemical reaction, and particularly what we mean by *spontaneous* reaction. Our task would obviously be much easier if we could observe the behaviour of the individual atoms as the reaction proceeds; but this is, of course, impossible and so we can only infer what happens to the individual atoms from experimental measurements taken during the reaction, and by noting the types of product resulting from different types of reactants. We can certainly measure the *rate* at which the reaction proceeds — this is the field of reaction kinetics — but having done so we still do not know *why* the reaction occurs in the first place. Hence, although a knowledge of the rate of a reaction is often invaluable to the chemist, it does not lead us any nearer to an understanding of what the driving force of the reaction is. Therefore we shall not be concerned in this book with a study of the factors affecting the rate of a chemical reaction, but with an investigation of what makes the reaction *spontaneous*.

It is unfortunate that in much elementary chemical literature the word 'spontaneous' is usually only used of those reactions which take place immediately contact is made between the reactants. For example, a substance is said to be spontaneously inflammable if it bursts into flame as soon as it is exposed to the atmosphere. Although such a reaction is a spectacular example of spontaneity it represents only a small proportion of those reactions which are truly spontaneous. It has been suggested elsewhere that a more accurate meaning of spontaneous is 'having the potential to proceed without the assistance of external agency'. Note that in this statement nothing is implied about the *rate* of the reaction or process. Thus it is possible for a reaction to be spontaneous and yet proceed at such a slow rate as to appear to be almost non-existent. An example of such a reaction is the familiar combination of hydrogen and oxygen. These gases may be mixed at room temperature and kept for many years before reaction is at all appreciable, though the reaction *is* taking place albeit at an imperceptibly slow rate. The rate of the reaction can be increased by the addition of finely divided platinum so that the combination becomes explosive, but this does not alter the point that the reaction remains spontaneous with or without the catalyst. A second example illustrating a truly spontaneous reaction is that between lead and oxygen. It is readily recognised that the reaction between sheet lead and oxygen is a very slow one indeed, and even over a long period of time little reaction appears to take place. However, lead in a very finely-divided state (so-called pyrophoric lead, obtained by the action of heat on lead acetate) catches fire immediately it comes in contact with the air.

Both of the examples given show that the term 'spontaneous' when applied to chemical reaction is used in a special way, implying nothing about the rate of the reaction.

Hence our search for an answer to the question 'What is the driving force of a chemical reaction?' may begin with an examination of the factors which determine the direction of spontaneous reaction, for it is the *direction* of spontaneity which is one of the most important features of chemical reaction. We can best begin our investigation by looking closely at some simple examples of spontaneous processes which are familiar to us, and attempt to find out wherein lies the reason for their spontaneity.

Energy changes in spontaneous processes

It is an everyday experience that water flows downhill. If we were to pour some out of a container at the top of an incline it would *immediately* begin to flow down the slope. The process is a spontaneous one for it begins as soon as the water is poured out and it does not require any further external assistance, thus conforming to the definition of spontaneity suggested above. It is important to note that the *rate* at which the water flows is determined only by the angle of the slope and it does not affect the spontaneous nature of the process, for the water will always flow downhill no matter how steep the hill is. In a similar way a stone will fall to the ground if it is released some distance above it, a stretched piece of elastic will contract when released and a watch spring will gradually unwind. All of these processes may be described as spontaneous, for they occur of their own accord in one direction only.

Thus water cannot flow uphill of its own accord, the stone does not rise from the ground by itself, the elastic is never seen to suddenly stretch itself nor does the watch spring wind itself up. Although the spontaneous processes mentioned above never reverse themselves, it is of interest to note that they *can* be reversed by the employment of an external agency. The water may be pumped uphill, the stone may be projected into the air from a catapult, the elastic may be pulled out and the watch spring wound up. We are therefore led to our first statement concerning spontaneous processes, which may be expressed as follows:

A spontaneous process is of itself irreversible, and can only be reversed when work is done *on* the system.

(This is basically an expression of the second law of thermodynamics, to which we shall return in a later chapter.)

If we look closely at each of these processes we can see at once that a feature common to all of them is a net decrease in potential energy in the direction of spontaneous change. This energy may be lost from the system and utilised to do work of some kind (an elastic band may be used to drive a small toy, and the watch spring drives the hands of the watch), or it may be converted into another form of energy (kinetic energy in the case of the water and the falling stone).

By analogy we may therefore postulate that a chemical reaction will be spontaneous in a given direction because in passing from reactants to products a decrease in potential energy has taken place.[1]

It is obvious that if there is a decrease in potential energy in passing from reactants to products then this energy must be lost from the system in some way, presumably as heat. Thus towards the end of the nineteenth century Thomsen and Berthelot (in his *Essai de mecanique chimique*, 1878) suggested that the change in energy as measured by the heat evolved in a chemical reaction was the driving force behind the reaction. In support of this proposal they were able to cite many reactions in which heat is evolved in passing from reactants to products. Such reactions are known as *exothermic* reactions and are quite common. Hence, when one mole of graphite is completely burned in oxygen 94·0 kilocalories of heat are given out. This may be written as:

$$\underset{\text{(graphite)}}{C} + \underset{\text{(g)}}{O_2} = \underset{\text{(g)}}{CO_2} + 94 \cdot 0 \text{ kcal}$$

Since energy is *lost* by the system, it is conventional to say that the change in 'heat content' of the reaction (given the symbol ΔH) is negative. Thus for the reaction quoted above $\Delta H = -94 \cdot 0$ kcal (the negative sign indicating that the forward reaction is an exothermic one). Other examples of exothermic reactions, in which the heat change is for the mole quantities as expressed in the equation, are:

$$\underset{\text{(g)}}{N_2} + \underset{\text{(g)}}{3H_2} = \underset{\text{(g)}}{2NH_3} \qquad \Delta H = -22 \cdot 0 \text{ kcal}$$

$$\underset{\text{(g)}}{2H_2} + \underset{\text{(g)}}{O_2} = \underset{\text{(l)}}{2H_2O} \qquad \Delta H = -136 \cdot 6 \text{ kcal}$$

$$\underset{\text{(c)}}{Zn} + \underset{\text{(aq)}}{CuSO_4} = \underset{\text{(c)}}{Cu} + \underset{\text{(aq)}}{ZnSO_4} \qquad \Delta H = -50 \cdot 2 \text{ kcal}$$

The decrease in energy in passing from reactants to products may be illustrated for any exothermic reaction on an energy diagram as shown in Fig. 1.

[1] One of the most interesting proposals of this kind which was first made was by Sir Isaac Newton, whose interest in gravitational attractions led him to suggest in 1701 that chemical reactions took place because of a difference in gravitational attractions between the molecules of the reactants and those of the products.

It is important that before we go any further we understand exactly what the heat evolved in any reaction really represents. By reference to Fig. 1 we can appreciate that ΔH is the TOTAL energy change for that reaction in the sense that it sums up all the energy changes which take place in going from reactants to products. It can also be readily seen that the value of ΔH depends only on the values of E_p and E_r, and is independent of any intermediate stages in the course of the reaction. The significance of these points will become obvious later.

Thus the proposition that the driving force behind a chemical reaction is the decrease in energy in passing from reactants to products seems reasonable enough on the evidence which has been presented so far.

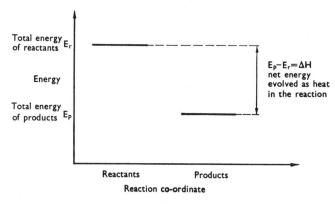

Fig. 1

Endothermic reactions

However, the proposition no longer remains tenable when we discover that there are many spontaneous chemical changes which are accompanied by an *absorption* of heat from the surroundings. That is to say that in passing from reactants to products there is an *increase* in the total energy of the system. Such reactions are known as *endothermic* reactions, and a few examples are given below:

$$\begin{array}{cccc} C & +H_2O & = CO & +H_2 \qquad \Delta H = +29\cdot 0 \text{ kcal} \\ \text{(graphite)} & \text{(g)} & \text{(g)} & \text{(g)} \end{array}$$

(Note that the sign of ΔH is now positive, since energy is *gained* by the system.)

Again,

$$\begin{array}{ccc} H_2 & +I_2 & = 2HI \qquad \Delta H = +12\cdot 8 \text{ kcal} \\ \text{(g)} & \text{(c)} & \text{(g)} \end{array}$$

and,

$$\begin{array}{ccc} C & +2S & = CS_2 \qquad \Delta H = +30\cdot 6 \text{ kcal} \\ \text{(graphite)} & \text{(l)} & \text{(l)} \end{array}$$

The increase in energy during endothermic reactions may be represented on an energy diagram as shown below (Fig. 2):

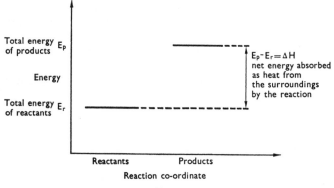

FIG. 2

Therefore it becomes obvious that while the decrease in energy may be a contributory factor to the driving force behind the reaction, it is not a sufficient one for all cases, particularly endothermic reactions.

Thus we must look yet again at more spontaneous processes, perhaps of a different kind, to discover what other factors may be involved.

Entropy changes in spontaneous processes

Since we have already established the energy factor in spontaneous reaction, we should obviously find it most convenient to turn our attention to systems in which there is little or no change in total energy during reaction. A system in which the total energy remains constant is known as an *isolated* system, and we shall now examine spontaneous changes in such a system.

The diffusion of two gases into each other is a process which will serve our purpose well at the present time. The process is a spontaneous one, for it begins as soon as the gases are placed in contact and it is irreversible. We can ensure that there is no change in total energy of such a process by carrying it out in a closed container which is suitably lagged, as illustrated in Fig. 3:

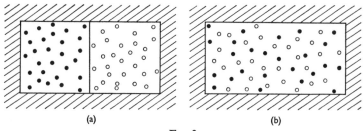

FIG. 3

In Fig. 3(a) the left-hand compartment contains a sample of 'black' gas at a given temperature and pressure, whilst the right-hand compartment contains a sample of 'white' gas at the same temperature and pressure. The two gases are separated by a movable partition. When the partition is withdrawn, as in Fig. 3(b), the gases begin to diffuse into each other and after a period of time diffusion will be complete.

If we ask ourselves what essentially is happening during such a change we are forced to realise that the system is becoming more 'mixed up'. Before the partition was removed it was possible to say with absolute certainty that all the molecules of 'black' gas were in the left-hand half of the box, and all the molecules of 'white' gas were in the right-hand half. However, after the removal of the partition, with the consequent diffusion, it is no longer possible to make such a statement. The probability of a chosen molecule of either gas occupying a given volume of space has decreased during the change, and we say that the system has become less predictable or more chaotic.

A related process is the expansion of an ideal gas into a vacuum. The process is again spontaneous for it does not require any external assistance and it is naturally irreversible — a gas will not contract in volume of its own accord. (The reverse process may be brought about, however, by the application of a piston.) Again, the change is accompanied by an increase in what we shall call the 'degree of disorder' of the system.

We may now formulate another proposition concerning the nature of spontaneous processes, especially for those taking place in isolated systems. For such processes there is always a tendency for the system to become more disordered, and this factor would appear to become the criterion for spontaneous change. We say that for such a change there has been an increase in the ENTROPY of the system. Although we have equated the term 'entropy' with the degree of disorder of the system, it is, in fact, a fundamental thermodynamic concept, as will be shown in a later chapter.

For the present we may say that if a system is very disordered it will have a high entropy, whereas if it is a very orderly system it will have a low entropy value. Therefore a gas, which is composed of particles moving in random motion, will tend to have a relatively high entropy; whereas a solid, with a regular crystalline structure, will tend to have a low entropy. We may note here that any system which is perfectly ordered will have the lowest entropy of all — zero entropy (for example a pure crystalline substance at absolute zero of temperature). We shall return to this point again in a later chapter when the more fundamental definition of entropy is discussed.

Our criterion therefore becomes:

for spontaneous change in an isolated system there must be an increase in entropy.

The universe itself may be considered an isolated system of constant energy, and so it follows that for all changes in the universe taken as a whole there must be a net increase in entropy, although in different parts of the universe there may be changes taking place which involve either an increase or decrease in entropy or no change in entropy at all. Thus although the energy of the universe is constant, the entropy must continually be increasing.

Entropy is usually given the symbol S, and therefore for spontaneous change in such a system ΔS must be positive.

So far as a chemical reaction is concerned this entropy change comes about because a reaction is simply a rearrangement of atoms or ions from one pattern (in the reactants) to another (in the products). If the structure of the products is very much more disordered than that of the reactants there will be a resultant increase in entropy, and vice versa. This increase in entropy may well be the motivating force behind the reaction.

Types of systems

We cannot assume, however, that all chemical reactions are the isolated systems which we have discussed above. In fact most chemical reactions fall into the category of *closed* systems (where there may be exchange of energy but not of matter with any other system), and other reactions fall into the category of *open* systems (where there is exchange of both energy and matter with other systems). Therefore, if for most chemical reactions there are changes in both energy and entropy, it becomes quite clear that neither a decrease in heat energy nor an increase in entropy can *alone* determine the direction of spontaneous change for those reactions.

The stretching of rubber

A familiar example of a system which involves both energy and entropy changes simultaneously is the stretching and contracting of rubber. When rubber in the stretched state is released it quickly contracts, and use may be made of this contraction to do work of some kind, for example, the driving of a small toy by a rubber band. Thus the system loses potential energy.

The change in entropy during the contraction can be accounted for as follows. X-ray diffraction patterns of rubber in the stretched and unstretched conditions have shown that whereas in the stretched state a definite fibre structure is apparent, in the unstretched state the structure is a random one. Now rubber is composed of a large number of isoprene units (C_5H_8), joined up as illustrated in Fig. 4:

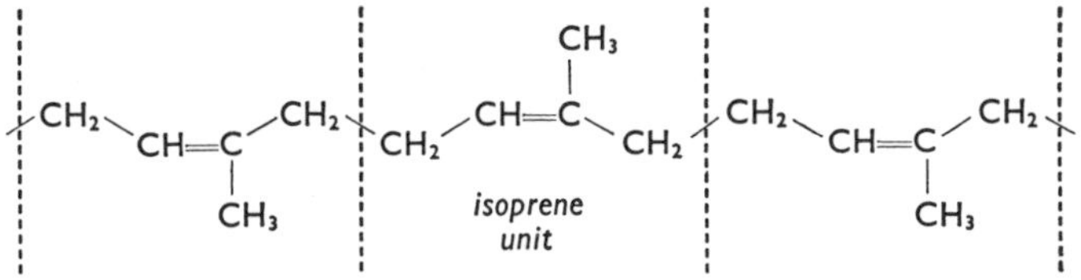

FIG. 4

In the stretched state the long hydrocarbon chains are pulled into an ordered alignment, whereas in the unstretched state the chains are irregularly

coiled around each other in a more random fashion. A model of this is
shown in Fig. 5:

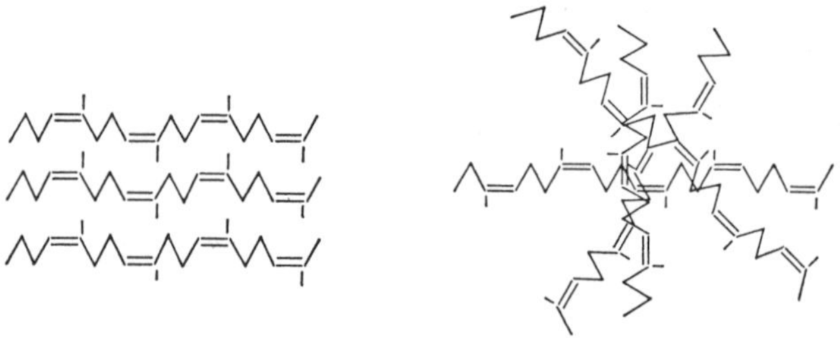

(a) Stretched form　　　　　　　(b) Unstretched form

Fig. 5

Clearly the stretched state is much more ordered than the unstretched state
and therefore in contracting the system is experiencing an increase in
entropy. It is of interest to note that wool, which is unlike rubber in properties, has a regular structure in both the stretched and unstretched forms.
In the case of the contraction of rubber we have seen that the process is
accompanied by both an increase in entropy and a decrease in potential
energy, and therefore we should expect the change to take place spontaneously in the direction it does.

Dissolution of ammonium nitrate

Another example of a system which experiences a change in both energy
and entropy is the dissolution of ammonium nitrate in water. That there is
a change in heat energy during this process can be verified merely by holding
a test-tube containing water in the hand while the solid is being added.
The absorption of heat by the system is obvious! The reason why heat is
absorbed during the process will be discussed later. Thus for this process
ΔH is fairly large and positive.

However, since the ammonium and nitrate ions are leaving their positions
on the crystal lattice and are adopting a more irregular disposition in
solution, the process will be accompanied by an increase in entropy. Thus
ΔS will be quite large and positive.

In this case it can be seen that the energy change and the entropy change
oppose each other in their influence on the direction of spontaneous change
within the system. It is obvious here that the entropy change is the dominant
one, but this need not necessarily be so in any other case.

Free energy changes

The problem which now presents itself is that of deciding *in advance* which
of the two factors, energy change or entropy change, will determine the
direction of spontaneous reaction if they are opposed to each other. We
have decided that a knowledge of either, by itself, is not sufficient for this
purpose.

Because of this a new function is defined which incorporates both the energy and entropy changes. The new function is given the symbol ΔG and is defined in terms of the change in total energy ΔH, the change in entropy ΔS, and the absolute temperature T at which the reaction takes place, in the following way:

$$\Delta G = \Delta H - T.\Delta S$$

Now we have already decided that ΔH measures the change in *total* energy during the reaction. The product $T.\Delta S$ (which is also an energy term since the equation must be dimensionally consistent) measures the change in energy which takes place as a result of the rearrangement of the constituent atoms. This 'internal' change in energy is always contained within the system and is therefore never available to do work outside it. Therefore ΔG is the difference between the total energy change and the 'unavailable' energy change ($\Delta H - T.\Delta S$) and is thus a measure of the energy which *is* available to do work outside the system, i.e. it is a measure of the 'free' energy. For this reason the term ΔG is known as the change in FREE ENERGY of the reaction.

It is important to realise that although this free energy is available to do work outside the system, the maximum amount of work can only be done when the change takes place 'reversibly'. Therefore if we would measure the free energy change for any reaction directly we must do so under 'reversible' conditions. The way in which this can be carried out in practice will be discussed later, together with a discussion of the meaning of 'reversible' and 'irreversible' as applied to such processes.

Now we have previously seen that for spontaneous change within a system of constant entropy the potential energy must decrease (the falling stone), and also for spontaneous change within a system of constant energy the entropy must increase (the diffusing gases). If both of these changes take place simultaneously in a given system, then we could reasonably assume that spontaneous change would take place (the stretching of rubber). Applying this to the free energy equation, we see that if ΔH is negative and ΔS is positive then since T is always positive (because it is measured in degrees absolute) ΔG must necessarily be negative.

A system in which both energy and entropy changes take place at constant temperature and pressure is the closed system to which many chemical reactions correspond. Thus the criterion for spontaneous change within a closed system is that there must be a decrease of free energy, i.e. ΔG must be negative. Note that this criterion cannot apply to an open system (which can exchange matter with other systems), for which no general criterion of spontaneous change is available.

Thus we are now in a position where we may suggest an answer to the problem which we originally set ourselves. This could be as follows:

The driving force for spontaneous chemical reaction is the decrease in free energy which takes place during the reaction.

The value of the relationship $\Delta G = \Delta H - T.\Delta S$ is that it does enable us to predict in advance whether a proposed chemical reaction will take place or not, provided that we know enough about the energy and entropy changes. Obviously if a proposed reaction is likely to be both exothermic and experience an increase in entropy, then ΔG would be large and negative and spontaneous reaction would be expected.

Conversely, if the reaction is likely to be endothermic and experience a decrease in entropy then ΔG would be positive and no reaction would be expected.

It is only when the influences of energy change and entropy change oppose each other that their relative magnitudes become important. Since the entropy term $T.\Delta S$ involves the multiplication of the entropy change by the absolute temperature, it can be readily seen that even when ΔS is relatively small in magnitude, the product $T.\Delta S$ will be quite large at high temperatures. Therefore we may say that although at ordinary temperatures the heat change may well determine the sign of ΔG (especially if ΔH is large), at high temperature it will be the entropy term which will be the determining factor. Thus for any reaction in which ΔS is positive the probability of the reaction taking place will increase with increasing temperature, and conversely, a negative ΔS implies that the reaction is more unlikely to take place as the temperature increases.

In what follows we shall be concerned with a more detailed study of the changes in heat energy, entropy and free energy which take place during chemical reaction. If we can evaluate these changes theoretically then we shall be in a much stronger position to predict quantitatively, instead of merely qualitatively, the direction of spontaneous reaction under a given set of conditions.

Part Two
Heat Changes in Chemical Reactions

2 Definitions, Conventions and Laws

Sign of the heat change
We have already seen, in Chapter 1, that the sign of a heat change is decided by reference to the evolution or absorption of heat *by the system*, i.e. the chemical reaction itself and not the surroundings. Thus we noticed that if the reaction was exothermic the sign of ΔH was negative, since the system lost energy, and vice versa.

Units in which heat changes are measured
The unit in which heat changes are most commonly expressed is the *kilocalorie* (i.e. the heat required to raise the temperature of one kilogramme of pure water from $15°$ C to $16°$ C). This is often abbreviated to 'kcal'. However, it may be that it will become more convenient to express the heat change in *joules*, or perhaps kilo-joules (kj), especially if the heat energy has to be related to other forms of energy.

Standard heat changes
No real meaning can be attached to the value of a heat change unless the exact conditions under which the measurement of the heat change took place are quite clearly stated. In particular it is important to state the physical condition of both the reactants and the products. This is normally done via the equation, indicating the states of the substances parenthetically, as illustrated in the equations in the first chapter. Thus the reaction

$$2H_2 \underset{(g)}{} + O_2 \underset{(g)}{} = 2H_2O \underset{(g)}{}$$

is quite distinct from the reaction

$$2H_2 \underset{(g)}{} + O_2 \underset{(g)}{} = 2H_2O \underset{(l)}{}$$

and the two reactions therefore have different values of ΔH. (For the first reaction $\Delta H = -114 \cdot 0$ kcal, whilst for the second reaction $\Delta H = -136 \cdot 6$ kcal.) The difference in these two values is, of course, due to the heat required to vaporise the water formed in the first case.

Whenever a substance taking part in a chemical reaction can exist in different structural modifications, the particular form employed in the reaction must also be clearly stated. For example, for the reaction

$$\underset{(graphite)}{C} + \underset{(g)}{O_2} = \underset{(g)}{CO_2}$$

$\Delta H = -94 \cdot 0$ kcal

Whereas for the reaction

$$\underset{(diamond)}{C} + \underset{(g)}{O_2} = \underset{(g)}{CO_2}$$

$\Delta H = -94 \cdot 5$ kcal

The equation is not only essential to show the physical states of the substances involved, but it also provides information as to the actual quantities of substances taking part. In Chapter 1 it was stated that the heat changes as quoted were for the mole reacting quantities as expressed by the equation, and it is quite evident that the magnitude of the heat change will vary according to the quantities of reagents taken.

In order to compare the heat changes of different reactions, or to make use of values of heat changes in thermochemical calculations, it is conventional to quote the magnitude of the heat change taking place at a chosen temperature. This is usually 25° C, although sometimes it is taken as 18° C. When a heat change is measured in such a way it is said to be the Standard Heat Change, and is usually denoted by $\Delta H°$. It is necessary from time to time to determine what the heat change for a given reaction would be at temperatures other than 25° C, and this information may be obtained by employing Kirchhoff's equation (see later).

Some special heats of reaction

We have seen that in order to express precisely the heat change of a chemical reaction we must state exactly the conditions under which the measurement was made. There are, however, certain types of chemical reaction which are defined, so far as their heat changes are concerned, in a special way.

The most general type of heat change which can be defined is simply called the 'Heat of Reaction', and this is defined as the heat change which takes place at 25° C when the reactants and products are in the mole proportions as indicated by the equation for the reaction. If gases are involved in the reaction it is usual to stipulate that these should be at one atmosphere pressure.

Heats of formation

Formation reactions are those in which a substance is prepared directly from its constituent elements. Thus the *Heat of Formation* of a compound is defined as the heat change when one mole of the compound is formed from its elements in the standard states (25° C and one atmosphere pressure).

It is conventional to take the actual heat contents of all elements in their standard states as zero. Thus the heat content of a given compound must be equal to its heat of formation $\Delta H_f°$. The heats of formation of some common compounds are given in Table 1.

TABLE 1

Compound (state)	CO_2 (g)	H_2O (l)	NH_3 (g)	C_2H_4 (g)	C_2H_6 (g)	H_2S (g)	MgO (c)
$\Delta H_f°$ kcal mole^{-1}	−91·4	−68·3	−11·0	+9·6	−23·4	−5·2	−143·8

Using a knowledge of the heat contents of the compounds and elements from their ΔH_f° values, the heats of reaction of many chemical changes can be calculated.

For example the heat of the reaction

$$\underset{\text{(g)}}{C_2H_4} + \underset{\text{(g)}}{H_2} = \underset{\text{(g)}}{C_2H_6}$$

may be calculated as follows. From Table 1 the heat of formation of ethylene is $+9\cdot6$ kcal mole^{-1}, and therefore we can say that the heat content of ethylene is $+9\cdot6$ kcal mole^{-1} since $9\cdot6$ kcal of heat are absorbed when one mole of ethylene is formed. In a similar way the heat content of ethane is $-23\cdot4$ kcal mole^{-1}.

Thus, writing the heat content of each species below its formula:

$$\begin{array}{ccc}
\underset{\text{(g)}}{C_2H_4} & + \underset{\text{(g)}}{H_2} & = \underset{\text{(g)}}{C_2H_6} \\
+9\cdot6 & 0 & -23\cdot4
\end{array}$$

the change in heat content for the whole reaction is given by:

$$\Delta H = -23\cdot4 - (+9\cdot6) \text{ kcal}$$

i.e.
$$\Delta H = -33\cdot0 \text{ kcal}$$

Heats of combustion

The heat change which takes place when one mole of a substance is completely burned in oxygen is known as the Heat of Combustion of the substance. We shall call it ΔH_c°, when standard conditions apply. Many of the compounds which have been studied are organic, for obvious reasons, and

TABLE 2

Substance	ΔH_c°	Substance	ΔH_c°
CH_4 (g)	$-212\cdot8$	CH_3OH (l)	$-170\cdot9$
C_2H_6 (g)	$-372\cdot8$	C_2H_5OH (l)	$-327\cdot0$
C_2H_4 (g)	$-337\cdot2$	$CH_3CO.CH_3$ (l)	$-427\cdot0$
C_2H_2 (g)	$-310\cdot6$	C_6H_{12} (l)	$-939\cdot0$
C_6H_6 (l)	$-783\cdot4$	$C_{12}H_{22}O_{11}$ (s)	$-1,360\cdot0$

Values are given in kcal mole^{-1} and are for the production of CO_2 (g) and H_2O (l).

most of these are the compounds containing carbon, hydrogen and oxygen. Table 2 gives the values of the heats of combustion of some familiar organic compounds.

Heats of dissociation

The Heat of Dissociation of a substance is the heat change which takes place when one mole of the substance is completely decomposed to form atoms of the constituent elements in the gas phase at $25°$ C and one atmosphere pressure.

In general, heat must be supplied in order to decompose a substance and therefore the heats of dissociation, ΔH_d°, are usually positive. Such values for some of the elements are given in Table 3.

TABLE 3

Equation for dissociation	ΔH_d° kcal mole^{-1} of substance
F_2 = 2F (g) (g)	$+36\cdot6$
Cl_2 = 2Cl (g) (g)	$+57\cdot8$
Br_2 = 2Br (l) (g)	$+53\cdot4$
I_2 = 2I (c) (g)	$+51\cdot0$
H_2 = 2H (g) (g)	$+104\cdot2$
O_2 = 2O (g) (g)	$+118\cdot4$
N_2 = 2N (g) (g)	$+225\cdot0$

We shall see later how these values are related to the 'bond energy' of the substances.

Heats of Neutralisation

The Heat of Neutralisation of an acid or an alkali is the heat evolved when that amount of the acid or alkali needed to form one mole of water is neutralised.

It is found that for all strong acids and bases the heat of neutralisation is approximately constant at -13.7 kcal per mole of water formed. The reason for this is that the process of neutralisation is that of the reaction

$$\underset{\text{(aq)}}{H^+} + \underset{\text{(aq)}}{OH^-} = \underset{\text{(l)}}{H_2O}$$

If both the acid and the alkali are strong they are present entirely as their ions, before reaction, and the salt formed will also be completely ionised. The net reaction in every case will be that described above.

In the case of weak acids and bases, complete ionisation will not take place and the heat evolved when one mole of water is formed will be less than 13.7 kcal. For acetic acid and sodium hydroxide 13.4 kcal of heat are evolved per mole of water, whilst for hydrochloric acid and ammonia the value is 12.7, and for acetic acid and ammonia it is 12.0 kcal.

Heat of Solution

The Heat of Solution of a substance is the heat change which takes place when one mole of substance is completely dissolved in a large enough volume of water so that no further heat change takes place. Under such conditions the solution is said to be at *infinite dilution*.

The process of dissolution of the solute in the solvent may take place in such a way that the solute is dissolved in only a small volume of solvent. In this case addition of more solvent to the solution formed would result in a further heat change, and this is known as the Heat of Dilution of the solute between the two solutions of specified concentration.

For example, when one mole of hydrogen chloride gas is dissolved in a large volume of water 18 kcal of heat are evolved. However, when one mole of gas is dissolved in water to produce a 12 M solution 14.2 kcal of heat are evolved. When this solution is diluted to a 6 M solution a further 2 kcal of heat are evolved. Heats of dilution are therefore much smaller in magnitude than heats of solution. More examples will be given in a later chapter when the mechanism of solution is examined in more detail.

Such reactions are usually represented thus:

$$\underset{\text{(g)}}{HCl} + aq = \underset{\text{(aq)}}{HCl} \qquad \Delta H = -18 \text{ kcal}$$

Laws of thermochemistry

Probably the earliest attempt to formulate a thermochemical law, which related in a quantitative way the heat changes taking place in chemical reactions, was that of Lavoisier and Laplace (1780) who suggested that the quantity of heat required to decompose a compound into its elements is equal in magnitude to the quantity of heat evolved when the same compound is formed from its elements. The sign of the heat change will, of course, not be the same in each case.

This law is, in fact, a corollary of a much more fundamental law which has become known as the *first law of thermodynamics*, which may be expressed in many ways, probably the simplest being that although energy may be converted from one form to another it cannot be created or destroyed. This statement is sometimes also known as the *law of conservation of energy* and it is based entirely on the experience that no process has ever been conceived in which a continuous production of mechanical work takes place without the supply of an equivalent amount of energy, i.e. it is impossible to create a perpetual motion machine. Thus if the law of Lavoisier and Laplace were not true then it would be possible to create energy by making a compound from its elements and then decomposing it back to the same elements.

It follows therefore that any thermochemical equation may be reversed provided that the sign of the heat change is reversed, the magnitude remaining the same, of course. From the equation

$$\underset{\text{(graphite)}}{C} + \underset{\text{(g)}}{O_2} = \underset{\text{(g)}}{CO_2} \qquad \Delta H = -94 \text{ kcal}$$

may be written the equation

$$\underset{\text{(g)}}{CO_2} = \underset{\text{(graphite)}}{C} + \underset{\text{(g)}}{O_2} \qquad \Delta H = +94 \text{ kcal}$$

A second thermochemical law which is derived directly from the first law of thermodynamics is Hess's Law. It is so called because it was discovered by G. H. Hess in 1840 when he was investigating the heat changes taking place at each step during the synthesis of given chemical compounds. He found that the heat content change involved in the conversion of one chemical compound to another was independent of the way in which the conversion was carried out. He stated his law (sometimes also known as the *law of constant heat summation*) as follows:

> The change in heat content accompanying a chemical reaction is independent of the pathway between the initial and final states.

Consequently, once the initial and final states of a given chemical system are fixed the heat change is also fixed. If this were not so then it would be possible to create energy by carrying out a reaction and then returning to the original states by a different pathway. This is contrary to the first law of thermodynamics.

Hess's law may be illustrated diagrammatically as in Fig. 6.

The energy diagram indicates that the conversion of A into E may be carried out either directly, when the heat change is ΔH_1, or via the intermediate substances B, C and D. In the latter case it can easily be seen that the net heat change is $\Delta H_2 + \Delta H_3 + \Delta H_4 + \Delta H_5$ (taking due regard of the sign of the heat change). It is obvious that

$$\Delta H_1 = \Delta H_2 + \Delta H_3 + \Delta H_4 + \Delta H_5$$

which is an expression of Hess's Law. It must be emphasised that an *algebraic* summation of the heat changes must be made.

It will readily be appreciated that if four of the terms in the above equation are known then the fifth may be calculated. Thus the application of Hess's law often allows the determination of the heat change of a reaction which cannot be measured directly. An example will illustrate this.

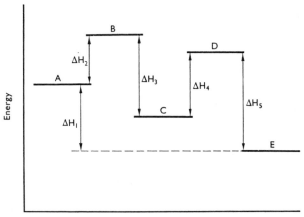

Fig. 6

Example

Calculate the heat of formation of gaseous ammonia given that the heat of combustion of ammonia is 75·7 kcal (evolved) and the heat of formation of steam is 57·8 kcal (evolved).

We are required to find the heat change associated with the equation

$$\tfrac{1}{2}N_2 + \tfrac{3}{2}H_2 = NH_3$$
$$(g) \qquad (g) \qquad (g)$$

Let this heat change be designated as ΔH_f°. We know that the heat of combustion of ammonia is 75·7 kcal and this corresponds to

$$NH_3 + \tfrac{3}{4}O_2 = \tfrac{3}{2}H_2O + \tfrac{1}{2}N_2 \qquad \Delta H = -75\cdot7 \text{ kcal}$$
$$(g) \qquad (g) \qquad (g) \qquad (g)$$

Therefore, according to the first law of thermodynamics we can write

$$\tfrac{3}{2}H_2O + \tfrac{1}{2}N_2 = NH_3 + \tfrac{3}{4}O_2 \qquad \Delta H = +75\cdot7 \text{ kcal}$$
$$(g) \qquad (g) \qquad (g) \qquad (g)$$

(Equation 1)

We also know that

$$H_2 + \tfrac{1}{2}O_2 = H_2O \qquad \Delta H = -57\cdot8 \text{ kcal}$$
$$(g) \qquad (g) \qquad (g)$$

Therefore

$$\tfrac{3}{2}H_2 + \tfrac{3}{4}O_2 = \tfrac{3}{2}H_2O \qquad \Delta H = -86 \cdot 7 \text{ kcal}$$
$$\text{(g)} \qquad \text{(g)} \qquad \text{(g)}$$

(Equation 2)

Adding equations 1 and 2 we obtain:

$$\tfrac{3}{2}H_2O + \tfrac{1}{2}N_2 + \tfrac{3}{2}H_2 + \tfrac{3}{4}O_2 = NH_3 + \tfrac{3}{4}O_2 + \tfrac{3}{2}H_2O$$
$$\text{(g)} \qquad \text{(g)} \qquad \text{(g)} \qquad \text{(g)} \qquad \text{(g)} \qquad \text{(g)} \qquad \text{(g)}$$

i.e.

$$\tfrac{1}{2}N_2 + \tfrac{3}{2}H_2 = NH_3$$
$$\text{(g)} \qquad \text{(g)} \qquad \text{(g)}$$

the formation of gaseous ammonia.

Adding the heat changes in equations 1 and 2, and applying Hess's law to equate this to ΔH_f°, we obtain

$$\Delta H_f^{\circ} = +75 \cdot 7 + (-86 \cdot 7) \text{ kcal}$$
$$= -11 \cdot 0 \text{ kcal}$$

The heat of formation of gaseous ammonia is 11 kcal (evolved).

We shall see later how a further application of the first law of thermodynamics, in the form of the Born–Haber cycle, may be used in the calculation of energy changes which are difficult to measure directly.

Effect of external conditions on the heat change

Having taken the precaution of writing the correct equation, together with the relevant state symbols, and stating the temperature for the reaction taking place, the heat change will not be completely defined unless the external physical conditions, especially those of pressure and volume if gaseous substances are involved, are clearly stated.

Thus if a reaction takes place under constant volume conditions (closed container), the heat change, usually given the symbol ΔU, may be different from that of the same reaction measured under conditions of constant pressure (usually one atmosphere) given the symbol ΔH. Consider a given reaction taking place separately at constant volume and constant pressure (see Fig. 7):

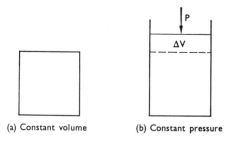

(a) Constant volume   (b) Constant pressure

FIG. 7

In Fig. 7(a) the reaction is depicted as taking place at constant volume and the heat change, as measured by the corresponding temperature change, gives a value for ΔU. In Fig. 7(b) the reaction is allowed to take place under constant pressure conditions and there is a volume change in addition to the temperature change. If the external pressure is P, and the change in volume is ΔV, then the external work done by the system in expanding (in this case) will be $P.\Delta V$. Now since work is being done *by* the system the difference between ΔU and ΔH will be equal to the work done, and so we may write:

$$\Delta H = \Delta U + P.\Delta V$$

The sign of the term $P.\Delta V$ is positive since work is done *by* the system, and for exothermic reactions the sign of ΔU and ΔH is negative.

For those reactions which involve only solids and liquids the volume change ΔV is so small that the term $P.\Delta V$ is negligible in comparison with ΔH and ΔU, and therefore it can be ignored. When gases are involved however, the volume change may be quite large, and the difference between ΔH and ΔU becomes significant.

Applying the gas laws to one mole of gas, we have:

$$P.V = R.T$$

where R is the ideal gas constant and T is the absolute temperature. For n moles of gas:

$$P.V = n.R.T$$

We may now write:

$$P.\Delta V = \Delta n.R.T$$

where Δn is the change in the number of moles of gas causing the change ΔV in volume.

Substituting in the first equation above:

$$\Delta H = \Delta U + \Delta n.R.T$$

This last relationship makes it possible to calculate the magnitude of the heat change at either constant volume or constant pressure, knowing the equation for the reaction and the conditions under which the reaction takes place together with the value for ΔH or ΔU whichever is relevant.

Note that in the case of an *increase* in volume at constant pressure, when Δn will be positive, if the reaction is exothermic then ΔH will be smaller in magnitude than ΔU, and vice versa. When there is no volume change even in the gaseous state, then ΔH will equal ΔU. An example should make the method of calculation clear.

Example

The heat of combustion of gaseous ethylene to form carbon dioxide and liquid water at 27° C and under a constant pressure of one atmosphere is 337 kcal mole^{-1}. Calculate the heat of reaction at constant volume at

27° C. Assume a value of 2 cal mole^{-1} deg^{-1} for the gas constant R. (O & C 'S' Level, part question, 1965.)

The equation for the combustion is:

$$CH_2{=}CH_2 \underset{(g)}{+3O_2} \underset{(g)}{= 2CO_2} \underset{(g)}{+2H_2O} \underset{(l)}{}$$

Since one mole of ethylene is involved in the reaction as written, then the heat change will be 337 kcal (evolved).

Thus $\Delta H = -337$ kcal.

Ignoring the small volume of liquid water formed in the reaction, the total change in the number of moles of gas, Δn, equals $2-4$, i.e. -2 moles. The negative sign indicates that there is a contraction in volume. Therefore the work done *on* the system is given by:

$$\Delta n.R.T = -2.2.300 \text{ cal}$$
$$= -1,200 \text{ cal}$$
$$= -1·2 \text{ kcal}$$

Applying
$$\Delta H = \Delta U + \Delta n.R.T$$
$$-337 = \Delta U - 1·2$$
$$\Delta U = -337 + 1·2$$
$$= -335·8 \text{ kcal}$$

Therefore the heat of combustion of gaseous ethylene at constant volume at 27° C is 335·8 kcal mole^{-1}.

We have already noted in the first chapter that the majority of chemical reactions which we meet in the laboratory take place under conditions of constant pressure, rather than constant volume. Therefore in what follows the heat changes for reactions will be quoted as ΔH unless otherwise stated.

For those reactions which take place at constant volume no work is done either *by* the system or *on* the system, and so the heat change either increases or decreases the *internal* energy of the system. For this reason the term ΔU is often referred to as the 'change in internal energy'. In addition, the term ΔH, the change in heat content, is also described as the change in 'enthalpy'.

The effect of temperature on heat changes

We have already seen that if heat changes for different reactions are to be compared, it is necessary to refer each ΔH value to the same temperature, usually 25° C. We shall now examine how the value of ΔH changes when the temperature is varied.

Heat capacity

The quantity of heat which is required to raise the temperature of a system by 1° C is known as the *heat capacity* of the system, and is normally given the symbol C. If the substance is pure and has a mass of one gram, then this quantity of heat is known as the 'specific heat', but if the mass of substance is one mole then it is known as the 'molar heat capacity'.

For many solid elements at room temperature, it was found by Dulong and Petit (1819) that the heat capacity per gram-atom was approximately constant, at $6 \cdot 2 (\pm 0 \cdot 4)$ cal deg^{-1}. Table 4 gives the values for some common elements.

TABLE 4

Element	Li	Ca	Fe	Ag	I	Hg	U	B
Heat capacity per gram-atom	6·4	6·0	6·2	6·0	6·6	6·6	6·4	2·5

It will be seen that the metallic elements in the above table have heat capacities around 6·2, but boron, a non-metallic element, has an exceptionally low value. Other elements which also have low values are beryllium, silicon, phosphorus and carbon.

Now we have already seen that heat can be supplied to raise the temperature of a gas in two ways, at constant pressure and at constant volume. The molar heat capacity at constant pressure is given the symbol C_p, and that at constant volume C_v. In theory the difference between C_p and C_v is a constant, i.e. $C_p - C_v = R$, the gas constant. Some values are given in Table 5.

TABLE 5

Gas	Hydrogen	Oxygen	Ammonia	Carbon dioxide
C_p cal deg^{-1}	6·871	6·989	8·770	8·890
C_v cal deg^{-1}	4·884	4·994	6·700	6·860
$C_p - C_v$	1·987	1·995	2·070	2·030

Kirchhoff's equation

In order to derive a relationship between the heat of reaction and temperature change we shall consider a chemical reaction in which the reactants, represented by A, are converted to products B. The reaction is such that the initial temperature is T_1 and the final temperature is T_2. The change may be brought about in two ways. This is represented in Fig. 8, when constant pressure conditions prevail throughout.

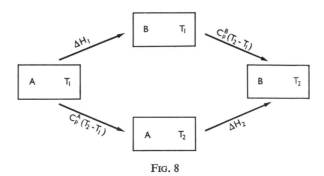

FIG. 8

Let us suppose that the heat of reaction at T_1 is ΔH_1, and at T_2 is ΔH_2. The alternative ways of bringing about the reaction are as follows:

(a) The conversion of A to B is carried out at constant temperature T_1. The heat change involved is therefore ΔH_1. The temperature of the products B is raised from T_1 to T_2. The heat required for this process will be $C_p^B.(T_2-T_1)$, where C_p^B is the heat capacity of the products at constant pressure.

Hence the total heat change is $\Delta H_1 + C_p^B.(T_2-T_1)$

(b) The temperature of the reactants A is raised from T_1 to T_2 at constant pressure. The heat required for this process will be $C_p^A.(T_2-T_1)$. The reactants A at temperature T_2 are converted to products B at temperature T_2, the heat change being ΔH_2.

Hence the total heat change is $\Delta H_2 + C_p^A.(T_2-T_1)$

According to Hess's law, since the initial and final states are the same for the two processes, the total heat change must be the same in each case. Therefore,

$$\Delta H_1 + C_p^B.(T_2-T_1) = \Delta H_2 + C_p^A.(T_2-T_1)$$
$$\Delta H_2 - \Delta H_1 = (C_p^B - C_p^A).(T_2-T_1)$$

i.e. we can write
$$\frac{d(\Delta H)}{dT} = \Delta C_p$$

where ΔC_p is the difference in molar heat capacities between the products and the reactants. This relationship between the heat of the reaction and temperature is known as Kirchhoff's equation, after Kirchhoff who first derived it in 1858.

For reactions at constant volume, a similar equation may be derived in an analogous way, and it is

$$\frac{d(\Delta U)}{dT} = \Delta C_v$$

In order to make use of the above equations for the calculation of heats of reaction at different temperatures it is necessary to integrate them between the limits of the temperature range concerned. The constant pressure case only will be shown.

From
$$\frac{d(\Delta H)}{dT} = \Delta C_p$$

Integrating between temperatures T_1 and T_2

$$\Delta H_2 - \Delta H_1 = \int_{T_1}^{T_2} \Delta C_p . dT$$

In order to evaluate the integral it is essential to know exactly in what way the heat capacities of the substances concerned in the reaction are dependent on temperature. Generally the heat capacity varies with temperature according to the equation:

$$C_p = a + bT + cT^2 + \ldots$$

In the above power series a, b, c etc. are constants for a given substance and T is the absolute temperature. Tables of the values of such constants for different substances are readily available, and recently tables of variation of ΔH with temperature based on the above over a wide range of temperatures have been drawn up.

If the Kirchhoff equation is integrated between the absolute zero of temperature and any other temperature T, then:

$$\Delta H - \Delta H_0 = \int_0^T \Delta C_p . dT$$

Assuming that the heat capacity equation holds at absolute zero, then at this temperature:

$$\Delta H - \Delta H_0 = 0$$

i.e. ΔH_0 is the hypothetical heat of reaction at absolute zero.

From what has been said above we may infer how the actual heat content of a substance will vary with temperature. If we suppose the heat content of a given substance at absolute zero is H_0 (its actual value is arbitrary since we can only measure changes in heat content), then we may infer that the heat content at any other temperature T is given by:

$$H = H_0 + \int_0^T C_p . dT$$

If during the process of raising the temperature of the substance from zero to T there is a change of state, then the expression for the heat content must contain a latent heat term (or two, if two changes in state occur). Hence we can write:

$$H = H_0 + \int_0^T C_p . dT + \text{latent heats}$$

Note also that if the heat capacity of the substance in one state is different from that in another then the integration must be carried out separately for each state.

This variation of heat content may be illustrated graphically as in Fig. 9.

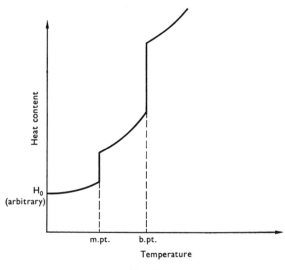

FIG. 9

3 The Measurement of Heat Changes

The choice of a method for the measurement of the heat change for a given reaction will depend very much on the particular reaction being investigated; for example whether solids, liquids or gases are involved, and what magnitude of heat changes are expected.

However, whatever method is used it is usual to employ a suitably designed reaction vessel, together with a device for the measurement of the temperature changes which will take place.

The measurement of temperature changes

For temperature changes of fairly high magnitude a calibrated thermometer is often employed and is sufficiently accurate in such cases. However, when the temperature change is small, and greater accuracy is required, as in the determination of heats of dilution for example, it will be necessary to find some alternative device. It is usual in such cases to use a thermocouple or a resistance thermometer. It may be possible in some instances to use a Beckmann thermometer, as in the freezing-point determinations. Whichever type is employed it is essential that the heat capacity of the instrument should be known, as this must be taken into account in the calculation. If possible the thermometer must have a low heat capacity, for obvious reasons.

The reaction vessel

The vessels in which heat changes are carried out are usually known as *calorimeters*. The design of such vessels will depend on the type of reaction being carried out, and this will be discussed shortly. In order to obtain accurate results it is necessary to take many precautions when constructing the calorimeter.

Chief among these is that of ensuring that the heat loss from the calorimeter by conduction, convection and radiation to the surroundings, is as small as possible. It is possible to avoid loss by convection with the use of an efficient stirring mechanism, which ensures that there is uniformity of temperature throughout the liquid. The loss of heat by conduction and radiation is kept at a minimum by surrounding the calorimeter with an outer jacket of some kind. One way in which this may be done is illustrated in Fig. 10.

The reaction vessel is a Dewar flask containing the liquid together with a thermometer and a stirrer S_1, which pass through a cork in the neck of the flask. The whole is supported on a cork base and immersed in a second vessel containing water maintained thermostatically at a constant temperature and stirred by S_2. Evaporation and convection losses are minimised by the cork and asbestos covers across the flask and outer vessel respectively. Radiation losses are small because of the air gap in the Dewar flask which is silvered for this purpose, and if the whole apparatus is surrounded by an insulating material heat losses are further controlled. Because the temperature of the outer vessel is maintained constant the rate of loss of heat is constant.

A similar type of calorimeter to the one described above, but which differs from it in one important respect, is the *adiabatic* calorimeter. In this calorimeter the temperature of the outer jacket is controlled so that it is always the same as the liquid in the Dewar flask. Thus the heat losses due to radiation and convection are negligible. This type of calorimeter is particularly useful when slow reactions are to be studied, for in a calorimeter of the first type it is essential that the heat change should take place rapidly.

The calorimeters described briefly above are obviously suitable for reactions taking place in solution, but would be unsuitable for reactions between solids, or gases, or both. In these cases special calorimeters must be used.

One such calorimeter is the *bomb* calorimeter. This is used for the determination of heats of combustion, in which the substance is burned in

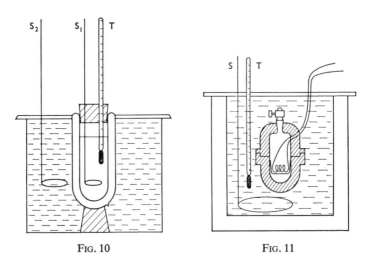

FIG. 10   FIG. 11

oxygen, and often for the heats of formation of many gaseous substances. It is illustrated in Fig. 11. It consists essentially of a cylindrical vessel, usually made of strong steel, lined internally with enamel to prevent oxidation of the steel, containing a platinum crucible into which is placed the solid to be burned in oxygen. An ignition coil is inserted in the solid and this usually consists of a very thin platinum wire which fuses when a suitable current is passed through it and ignites the solid. The whole vessel having been filled with oxygen at a known pressure via the inlet tube and valve, the combustion takes place usually very rapidly liberating heat which increases the temperature of the water in the surrounding vessel. The heat capacity of the bomb itself can be determined by burning a substance of known heat of combustion, benzoic acid being frequently used as a primary standard for this purpose. Many variations on the simple design of the bomb illustrated in Fig. 11 have been made, and the student is referred to a more specialised textbook for details of such devices. Corrections must be made for the heat liberated by the ignition coil when the current flows through it, the heat given out when the wire burns, and the heat developed by the paddles of the stirrer.

There are, of course, many other types of calorimeter, a rather different one being the ice calorimeter in which the volume change produced by the melting of ice is measured, and the heat evolved calculated from the known latent heat of ice, but sufficient examples have been given here to illustrate the general principles upon which the measurement of heat changes is made.

Determination of the calorimeter constant

We have already noted that it is important to know the heat capacity of any thermometer placed in the reaction vessel so that the heat absorbed by it may be allowed for in the calculation of the heat of the reaction. It is

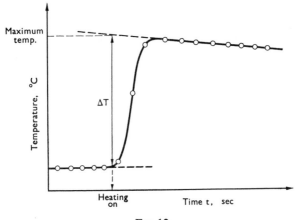

FIG. 12

obviously of vital importance that the heat capacity of the calorimeter itself is also determined, together with that of the stirrer used in the vessel. This is usually done in a preliminary experiment, when the total heat capacity of the calorimeter and its contents (stirrers and thermometer) is determined together. This is called the 'calorimeter constant'. This entails the supply of a known quantity of heat to the calorimeter and contents, usually containing also a known volume of water, and noting the maximum increase in temperature which results. The supply of heat is best made via a heating coil immersed in the water, when the quantity of heat is given by $I^2 Rt$ joules, where I is the current in amps, R is the resistance in ohms and t is the time in seconds. The maximum temperature may be determined by plotting a graph of temperature against time during the heating period, and continuing for some time after the current has been switched off, and extrapolating the graph as shown in Fig. 12.

If the cooling curve of the graph is projected back as far as the time when the current was switched on, the rise in temperature of the calorimeter and contents is given by ΔT. Hence the heat capacity of the system, i.e. the calorimeter constant, is given by $I^2 Rt/\Delta T$ joules deg^{-1}.

If possible it should be arranged that the volume of water used in the determination of the calorimeter constant should be the same as the volume of liquid used in the reaction being investigated. This is because the material of the calorimeter may be of low thermal conductivity and the area of the walls of the calorimeter in contact with the liquid will affect the calorimeter constant. Stirring is essential throughout the determination, and this should be done fairly slowly but regularly.

Practical exercises for the student

The experiments which follow have been included to illustrate the principles behind the measurement of the heats of reaction, and are not necessarily designed to obtain accurate results, although with care on the part of the student significant values may be obtained. For this reason it will be most convenient to use the simplest and most economic form of calorimeter, and the author has found the use of 'expanded polystyrene' calorimeters ideal for such experiments.

Polystyrene calorimeters

These are so named because use is made of the insulating properties of expanded polystyrene (often used in refrigerators nowadays in place of cork). The reaction vessel is a polythene squeeze bottle of about 60 cm³ to 70 cm³ capacity. These may be obtained cheaply from one of the large stores. This is embedded in a cube of expanded polystyrene, of side approximately 12 cm, as shown in Fig. 13. The thermometer also acts as a stirrer, provided care is taken when using it as such. Since the capacity of the bottle is above 60 cm³, solutions of up to 50 cm³ may be used with safety. The neck of the bottle is quite narrow and therefore it helps to avoid loss of heat by evaporation and prevents spilling of solution while stirring. The whole apparatus is very light, and very inexpensive to construct.

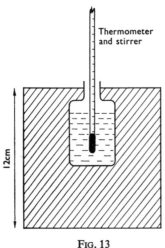

FIG. 13

Providing the reactions which are carried out are reasonably rapid ones, and efficient stirring is maintained the calorimeter will give reasonable results.

Experiment 1
The determination of the calorimeter constant

In order to make as realistic an estimate of the heat capacity of the calorimeter as possible, it is probably most convenient to carry out the method of mixtures. This can be done as follows.

Pipette 20 cm^3 of water at room temperature into the calorimeter. Place the thermometer in it and read the temperature when it remains steady. Warm some water in a beaker to a temperature about ten degrees higher than that in the calorimeter, measure this temperature accurately then *quickly* pipette 20 cm^3 of warm water into the calorimeter, stirring continuously during and after the addition. Note the maximum rise in temperature which takes place. There is probably no point in plotting a cooling curve to obtain a value for the maximum temperature in this case. Why not?

Calculation

The heat gained by the cold water when a rise in temperature of $T°$ C is observed is given by:

$$\text{heat gained} = \text{mass} \times \text{specific heat} \times \text{temperature rise}$$
$$= 20 \times 1 \times T \text{ cal}$$

In a similar way the heat lost by the hot water in falling in temperature by $t°$ C is given by:

$$\text{heat lost} = \text{mass} \times \text{specific heat} \times \text{temperature fall}$$
$$= 20 \times 1 \times t \text{ cal}$$

The difference in these two values is obviously the heat gained by the calorimeter and thermometer. Therefore assuming that the initial and final temperatures of the calorimeter was the same as the cold water:

$$\text{heat gained by calorimeter and thermometer}$$
$$= (20 \times t) - (20 \times T) \text{ cal}$$
$$= 20 \times (t - T) \text{ cal}$$

Therefore the heat capacity of the calorimeter and thermometer i.e. the calorimeter constant is given by:

$$\frac{20 \times (t - T)}{T} \text{ cal deg}^{-1}$$

Experiment 2
Heats of neutralisation of acids and bases

The aim of this experiment is to attempt to illustrate that the heats of neutralisation of strong acids by strong bases is approximately the same, and also that when weak acids and bases are used the heats of neutralisation are considerably lower than this value. The method remains the same in each case, and so only one experiment will be described.

The solutions of acids and bases used are conveniently made up to 2 M. This will facilitate the calculation and make rapid estimates of the heats of neutralisation possible.

Pipette 20 cm³ of 2 M acid into the bottle. Record the temperature of the acid when it is steady. Record also the temperature of a sample of 2 M alkali, and pipette 20 cm³ of this solution into the bottle as rapidly as possible, stirring continuously. Record the highest temperature attained.

Calculation

If the temperature of the acid and alkali before mixing are not the same, then an average value must be taken as the starting temperature. Suppose the increase in temperature is $\theta°$ C. In the following calculation it will be assumed that the specific heats of all solutions are unity, and that the specific gravities of the solutions are unity. This assumption is not as unjustified as would seem at first sight, for as the concentrations of aqueous solutions increase, the specific gravities increase while the specific heats decrease. In general, for dilute solutions these two effects cancel each other out, within the accuracy of the type of experiment being carried out here.

Therefore we may say that the heat gained by the acid $= 20 \times 1 \times \theta$ cal. This will also be the heat gained by the alkali, and therefore the total heat gained

$$= 40 \times 1 \times \theta \text{ cal}$$

Now if the acid and alkali are both monobasic, the admixture of 20 cm³ of each (of two molar concentration) would produce $\frac{1}{25}$ mole of water. Hence the heat evolved when one mole of water is formed will be:

$$25 \times 40 \times \theta \text{ cal}$$
$$= 1,000 \times \theta \text{ cal}$$
$$= \theta \text{ kcal}$$

Hence the rise in temperature conveniently gives the heat of neutralisation in kcal.

It is important, however, that we realise exactly what assumptions have been made in achieving this convenience. Apart from those assumptions outlined above it will have been observed that no allowance whatsoever has been made for the heat capacity of the calorimeter. What error is involved here? The temperature rise θ will be of the order of 12° C and so the heat gained by the solutions will be approximately $40 \times 12 = 480$ cal. Now the heat capacity of the polystyrene calorimeters is about 5 cal deg⁻¹, and hence the heat taken by the calorimeter will be approximately $5 \times 12 = 60$ cal. Hence the error involved is of the order of 10 per cent or more. It is therefore obvious that if a value of the heat of neutralisation of a given pair of reagents is required at all accurately then a full calculation must be carried out. But if it is only intended to illustrate the difference between strong acids and bases and weak acids and bases then the initial calculation will suffice. It is suggested that at least one 'accurate' determination should be made, and several different pairs of acids and bases compared. Note that if a dibasic acid is used for example, it will be necessary to take 20 cm³ of 1 M solution, since one mole of acid will produce two moles of hydrogen ions.

Experiment 3
Heat of the reaction

$$\text{Zn} + \text{Cu}^{2+} = \text{Zn}^{2+} + \text{Cu}$$
$$\phantom{\text{Zn}} \text{(c)} \quad \text{(aq)} \quad \text{(aq)} \quad \text{(c)}$$

Pipette 40 cm³ of a solution of M cupric sulphate into the polythene bottle. Record the temperature when steady. Weigh out enough zinc to ensure that the reaction goes to completion, i.e. at least $\frac{1}{25}$ mole. The zinc should preferably be in the form of dust. Why is this? The zinc dust should be added quickly, with stirring, to the cupric sulphate solution and the maximum temperature recorded. The increase in temperature is quite large in this case, and it may be worth while to find the maximum temperature graphically as already described.

Calculation

Suppose the maximum increase in temperature is $\theta°$ C. The heat gained by the solution and calorimeter (assumptions as in experiment 2) is given by:

$$(40 + c) \times \theta \text{ cal}$$

where c is the calorimeter constant. But this is the heat evolved when one twenty-fifth of a mole of cupric sulphate reacts; therefore the heat of reaction (one mole of cupric sulphate as in the equation) $= 25 \times (40 + c) \times \theta$ cal.

The effect on the magnitude of the heat change when zinc filings, or even granulated zinc is used instead of the dust, provides an interesting discussion point.

The reaction

$$\text{Zn} + 2\text{Ag}^+ = \text{Ag} + \text{Zn}^{2+}$$
$$\phantom{\text{Zn}} \text{(c)} \quad \text{(aq)} \quad \text{(c)} \quad \text{(aq)}$$

may be studied in a similar way, giving appreciable temperature increases.

Experiment 4
Heat of solution of ethanol in water

When ethanol dissolves in water heat is given out. The magnitude of the heat change will depend on the initial and final concentrations of the solution so formed. The greatest heat change will take place theoretically when the ethanol is dissolved in an infinite volume of water. This we have called the Heat of Solution. It is, of course, difficult to measure this directly because in such a large volume of water the temperature rise would be too small to measure, but it may be found indirectly by the determination of the heats of solution of one mole of ethanol in different volumes of water, and extrapolating the results to give the heat of solution at infinite dilution. This can be done as follows.

The mole weight of ethanol, C_2H_5OH, is 46 grams and that of water is 18 grams. Since the specific gravity of ethanol is 0·794 the mole volume will be 58 cm^3, whereas the mole volume of water will be 18 cm^3. Therefore by using a burette it will be possible to measure out different mole fractions of each compound, and to determine the heat change which takes place when these are mixed in the calorimeter. For example, measure out 9 cm^3 water into the polythene bottle from the burette. Record the initial temperature of the water. Record also the initial temperature of the ethanol which is contained in a second burette (fast flowing), and subsequently add, as rapidly as possible, 29·0 cm^3 of ethanol to the water, with stirring. Record the maximum rise in temperature and hence the difference in temperature ΔT, between the average initial temperature of the liquids and the final maximum temperature.

Calculation

The heat gained by the water $= 9 \times 1 \times \Delta T$ cal.

The heat gained by the alcohol $= 29 \times s \times \Delta T$ cal where s is the specific heat of ethanol.

The heat gained by the calorimeter $= c \times \Delta T$ cal, where c is the calorimeter constant.

Thus the total heat gained $= (9 + 29s + c) \times \Delta T$ cal.

In the case mentioned above this is the heat change for half a mole of alcohol in half a mole of water, therefore the heat change for one mole of alcohol in one mole of water will be twice this value. This is the heat of solution at that particular concentration.

The experiment should be repeated for different mole fractions of each substance, and a table of results drawn up as illustrated (see Table 6).

TABLE 6

Moles alcohol	Moles water	ΔT° C	ΔH per mole alcohol	$\dfrac{\text{moles water}}{\text{moles alcohol}}$
$\frac{1}{2}$	$\frac{1}{2}$			1
$\frac{1}{4}$	$\frac{3}{2}$			6
$\frac{1}{8}$	2			16
$\frac{1}{3}$	1			3
$\frac{1}{12}$	2			24
$\frac{1}{6}$	2			12
$\frac{1}{5}$	2			10
$\frac{1}{12}$	2·5			30

Note that whatever the number of moles of alcohol and water taken the total volume must not exceed 60 cm³ (capacity of polythene bottle). The figures given in Table 6 have been found to give satisfactory results.

When the different values of ΔH have been calculated they may be plotted on a graph as shown in Fig. 14.

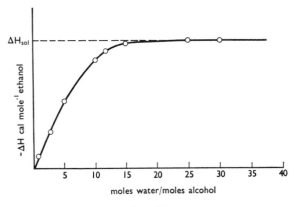

FIG. 14

If the straight portion of the graph is produced back to meet the ordinate axis the value of ΔH_{sol}, the heat of solution at infinite dilution, may be obtained, since the horizontal portion indicates that further dilution would produce no further heat change.

No allowance has been made in the above experiment for the decrease in volume which takes place when alcohol and water are mixed, for the accuracy of the experiment does not merit such a correction.

Experiment 5

The determination of the formula of cupric hydroxide by a thermochemical method

We have already seen how the heat change in a chemical reaction is dependant on the mole quantities of reactants. We may make use of this fact to determine the formula of cupric hydroxide.

Prepare standard solutions of 1M $CuSO_4$ and 2M KOH. Pipette 40 cm³ of alkali into the polythene bottle and record the temperature. Add, with stirring, 10 cm³ $CuSO_4$ solution of known initial temperature and observe the maximum temperature of the mixture. Repeat the experiment with 20 cm³ of alkali to 30 cm³ $CuSO_4$, again with 10 cm³ alkali to 40 cm³ of $CuSO_4$ and finally with 30 cm³ alkali and 20 cm³ of $CuSO_4$ solution.

Calculation

The results may be plotted graphically as shown below (Fig. 15).

Since we have taken the same total volume for each experiment, in the same apparatus, then the rise in temperature ΔT is proportional to the heat change taking place ΔH. Now the maximum heat change will take place when the two solutions react together in the mole proportions corresponding

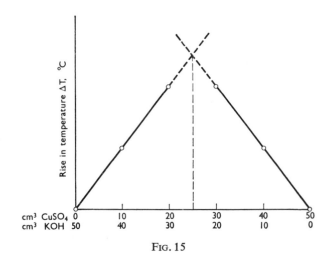

FIG. 15

to their stoichiometric formula. In the example given in Fig. 15 the maximum heat change takes place when 25 cm³ M $CuSO_4$ solution reacts with 25 cm³ 2M KOH solution. Therefore the mole reacting quantities are one mole $CuSO_4$ to two moles KOH. The equation for the reaction is therefore:

$$Cu^{2+} + 2\,OH^- = Cu(OH)_2$$
$$\text{(aq)} \qquad \text{(aq)} \qquad \text{(c)}$$

Note that the heat of the reaction corresponding to the above equation may easily be obtained from the results of this experiment. Other reactions may be studied in a similar manner using the same technique; it is known generally as the *continuous variation technique*.

4 Sources of Heat Changes

We have already seen how the heat change during a chemical reaction measures the *total* change in energy which takes place in proceeding from reactants to products. Now the total energy of any given set of reactants or products will be a sum of many different energy terms. These may be classified broadly as kinetic energies and potential energies.

Kinetic energy of a substance

If the molecules of the substance are free to move through space, as they would be in the gas phase and to a limited extent in the liquid phase, then the molecules would possess *translational* energy.

However if the molecule is capable of rotation about a principal axis then it would possess *rotational* energy, and this is illustrated for a diatomic molecule in Fig. 16.

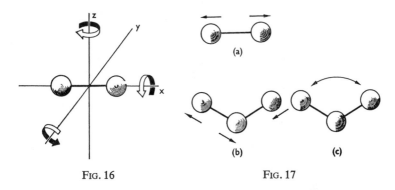

FIG. 16   FIG. 17

Note that rotation about the x axis is different from the other rotations in the case of a linear molecule, but this is not so for a polyatomic non-linear molecule in general. A single atom can only have one kind of rotation.

The molecule may possess *vibrational* energy in addition to translational and rotational energy. This arises from the vibrations of the atoms in the molecule in ways such as those illustrated in Fig. 17. In Fig. 17(a) the 'stretching' vibrations of a diatomic molecule are shown, similar vibrations for a non-linear molecule being illustrated in 17(b), while 17(c) shows a 'bending' vibration in a non-linear molecule. It will be obvious that a substance in the solid state will possess only kinetic energy of vibration, whereas a monatomic molecule in the gas phase will not possess any vibrational energy at all.

Now the translational energy can be regarded as being made up of three equal component energies in directions parallel to the three principal axes. The total translational energy per mole of substance is $\frac{3}{2}RT$, and so the energy in each of the three directions is $\frac{1}{2}RT$. This is in accordance with a principle known as the *equipartition of energy* (attributed to Maxwell), which expresses the way in which the total energy of a molecule is distributed among the different 'types' of energy, i.e. translational, rotational and vibrational. Each type of rotation contributes $\frac{1}{2}RT$ to the total energy (except the rotation about the x axis in the linear molecule shown in Fig. 16), and each vibration contributes RT per mole. Now for a non-linear molecule of n atoms, there are always three translational terms, three rotational terms and $3n-6$ vibrational terms. (For a linear molecule there are three translational, two rotational, and $3n-5$ vibrational terms.) The total energy of a mole of substance possessing all possible energy terms will therefore be of the order of $4RT$, that is to say at room temperature the energy will be about 2 or 3 kcal mole^{-1}.

Potential energy of a substance

If kinetic energy was the only kind of energy a substance possessed then the energy changes during chemical reactions would be very small indeed, for we have seen that the actual kinetic energy per mole of substance is only a few kcal. We know, however, from our measurement of the energy changes in chemical reactions that the magnitude of such changes can be of the order of a hundred kcal mole^{-1}. Thus some other energy term must contribute to the total energy of the substance. This is, in fact, a potential energy which arises from the forces which bind the atoms together in the substance. Therefore if we would study the factors which affect heat changes in chemical reactions we must examine the ways in which atoms combine together and the stability of such bonds when they are formed.

A. *Ionic bonds*

Lattice energy

Between any pair of oppositely charged ions in the gas phase there exist forces of attraction and repulsion. The attractions arise from the Coulombic forces between oppositely charged ions and also from the van der Waals forces (the first type diminishing with the square of the distance, the second with the seventh power of the distance). As a result of these forces the potential energy between the two ions decreases as they approach each other, (see Fig. 18, curve (a)). The repulsive forces which arise from the interaction of the electron clouds around the ions, diminish with distance to an even greater extent, and the potential energy of the ions increases as they approach each other (Fig. 18, curve (b)).

The attractive potential between two ions of charges z_1 and z_2 respectively, when they are at a distance r apart, can be expressed as:

$$E_{att} = \frac{-z_1 z_2 e^2}{r}$$

where e is the charge on the electron.

The repulsive potential may be similarly expressed as:

$$E_{rep} = \frac{b.e^2}{r^n}$$

where b is a constant dependent on the nature of the two ions concerned, and n is an integer.

Therefore the total potential energy between the two ions is given by the sum of these two terms, and will be:

$$-\frac{z_1 z_2 e^2}{r} + \frac{be^2}{r^n}$$

(The sign of the first term is negative since a decrease in potential energy takes place.) This summation is expressed by curve (c) in Fig. 18.

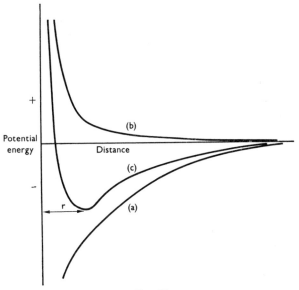

FIG. 18

Now in a crystal each ion experiences interaction with more than one other ion of opposite charge, for it is surrounded by many such ions, and therefore the potential energy associated with any one ion pair in a crystal may be written as:

$$E = -\frac{A z_1 z_2 e^2}{r} + \frac{Be^2}{r^n}$$

where A is a constant, known as the Madelung constant, which depends upon the type of crystal lattice, i.e. the arrangement of the ions around each other; the value of this constant for the sodium chloride lattice is 1·744 and that of the Wurtzite lattice is 1·641 for example. In order to obtain an expression for the total potential energy of the crystal we must multiply the above expression by Avogadro's number N_0, when the potential energy per mole of substance will be obtained.

This value is known as the *lattice energy* and reduces to:

$$\frac{N_0 \, A z_1 \, z_2 \, e^2}{r} \left(\frac{n-1}{n} \right)$$

where r is the equilibrium distance between the two ions in the crystal, as illustrated in Fig. 18. The value of n depends on the electronic configurations of the two ions in the crystal, for example for $1s^2$ $n=5$, for $2p^6$ $n=7$, for $3p^6$ $n=9$, and where the two ions are not isoelectronic the average value of n is used. In general, the more extensive the electron cloud the higher the value of n.

Thus we may define the lattice energy of a crystal as the energy required to separate the ions in one mole of crystal from their positions on the lattice an infinite distance apart in the gas phase.

We can see that the lattice energy depends mainly on two factors: the size of the ions (which determines r), and the charges on the ions, z_1 and z_2. Thus we would expect the strongest ionic bonding to take place between the smallest ions of highest charge. Some values of lattice energies are given in Table 7.

TABLE 7

Compound	Lattice energy (kcal mole⁻¹)	Compound	Lattice energy (kcal mole⁻¹)	Compound	Lattice energy (kcal mole⁻¹)
LiF	240	LiCl	193	CaF_2	620
NaF	215	NaCl	180	CaO	842
KF	190	KCl	164	MgF_2	690
RbF	182	RbCl	159	MgO	940
CsF	173	CsCl	149	MgS	778

From an inspection of the lattice energy values in Table 7 two main generalisations can be drawn.

(a) Effect of ionic size

The values for the alkali metals show that the greater the distance between the ions the lower the lattice energy. Thus LiF has a much greater lattice energy than CsF, and also than LiCl; again, MgO has a greater lattice energy than MgS. CaO has a greater lattice energy (842) than $CaCO_3$ (714), due to the larger size of the CO_3^{--} ion.

When the size difference between the cation and anion is large enough to allow direct contact between the cations (or the anions) then the lattice energy will be reduced owing to the repulsions between the similar ions.

For example in the lattice of lithium iodide the iodide ions are in contact and the lattice energy is therefore less than the theoretical value.

(b) Effect of ionic charge

We can see the effect of the ionic charge on the lattice energies of NaF, CaF_2, and CaO, where there is an increase in lattice energy corresponding to increased charges on the ions, the interionic distance remaining approximately the same for each compound.

Using the formula on page 42 it is possible to calculate theoretically what the lattice energy of a given ionic compound will be. However, the lattice energy may also be related to other thermodynamic quantities by means of a Born–Haber cycle, Fig. 19, which is really another expression of the first law of thermodynamics. The example in Fig. 19 is for an alkali halide.

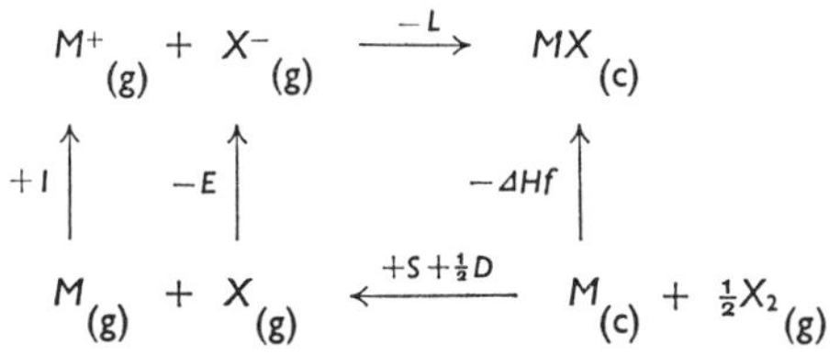

$$M^+_{(g)} + X^-_{(g)} \xrightarrow{\ -L\ } MX_{(c)}$$
$$+I \uparrow \qquad -E \uparrow \qquad -\Delta Hf \uparrow$$
$$M_{(g)} + X_{(g)} \xleftarrow{\ +S+\frac{1}{2}D\ } M_{(c)} + \tfrac{1}{2}X_2{}_{(g)}$$

Fig. 19

ΔH_f is the heat of formation of the compound as already defined, L is the lattice energy, E is the electron affinity of the halogen X (all these values being negative since they involve evolution of energy), S is the heat of sublimation of the metal M, I its ionisation potential, and D the heat of dissociation of the halogen.

Applying the first law to the cycle, we have:

$$-\Delta H_f = S + \tfrac{1}{2}D + I - E - L$$

and hence L may be calculated if the values of the remaining quantities are known or can be measured. It is important to note that initially lattice energies as calculated from the formula were substituted in the above equation to determine values for E, which are not otherwise easily obtained, but having obtained these values the cycle may be used for the computation of lattice energies.

When such values are compared with the purely theoretical ones there are often many distinct variations. These are due to departure from pure ionic character in the bonding. For example, in the compound MX the cation will exert an attraction on the electron cloud of the anion, and if this attraction is strong enough there will result partial sharing of electrons between M and X. The electron cloud of the anion becomes distorted and it is said to have been *polarised*.

Polarisation of ions

Fajans suggested that polarisation would be large if:

(i) the anion or cation is highly charged,

(ii) the cation is small and the anion is large.

(i) takes place because a cation with a high charge will attract electrons far more readily than one with a lower charge, and (ii) because if the cation is small it will be able to approach the anion more closely and if the anion is large the nucleus will have less attraction for the outermost electrons. Thus calcium carbonate is more easily decomposed than barium carbonate, since the percentage ionic character of $CaCO_3$ is less than that of $BaCO_3$ due to the more polarising Ca^{2+} ion.

The solubility of ionic compounds

When an ionic compound dissolves in a solvent the ions leave their ordered positions on the crystal lattice and become much more independent in solution, solvation taking place at the same time. This process of dissolution may be illustrated in the following way (Fig. 20):

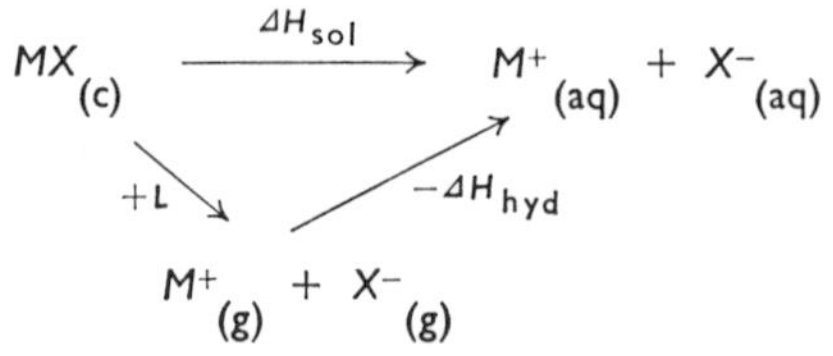

$$MX_{(c)} \xrightarrow{\Delta H_{sol}} M^+_{(aq)} + X^-_{(aq)}$$

$$+L \searrow \qquad \nearrow -\Delta H_{hyd}$$

$$M^+_{(g)} + X^-_{(g)}$$

FIG. 20

The heat of solution of the compound MX, ΔH_{sol}, is therefore determined by the relative values of the lattice energy L and the energy of hydration of the ions (if the solvent is water, as is most commonly the case). These energy terms oppose each other in that the energy necessary to separate the ions from the crystal lattice must be supplied from the heat given out during the hydration of the ions. If the heat of hydration of both ions taken together is represented by ΔH_{hyd} then we may write:

$$\Delta H_{sol} = L - \Delta H_{hyd}$$

Thus the heat of solution of an ionic compound in water depends on the relative values of L and ΔH_{hyd}. For most ionic compounds ΔH_{sol} is positive, that is heat is absorbed, and therefore the solubility of most salts in water increases with rise in temperature. Thus for one mole of sodium chloride $L = -184$ kcal and $\Delta H_{hyd} = +183$ kcal, therefore $\Delta H_{sol} = -1$ kcal, and the dissolution is accompanied by very little heat change. We saw how the dissolution of ammonium nitrate was accompanied by an absorption of heat in the first chapter. If the lattice energy is very high then dissolution of the compound may not take place at all; hence many fluorides tend to be less soluble than the corresponding chlorides since the smaller fluoride ions give a larger lattice energy (see Table 7). In the same way compounds with singly charged ions are more soluble than compounds with multiply charged ions, for example the alkaline earth metal salts are less soluble than the corresponding alkali metal salts. In general one may say that both lattice energy and hydration energy increase with increasing ionic charge, but the lattice energy usually shows the larger increase.

Summary

From the values of the lattice energies given in the tables it can be seen that if, during a chemical reaction, an ionic compound is either produced or destroyed then there will tend to be a correspondingly large change in energy. For example the reaction

$$\underset{\text{(c)}}{\text{Na}} + \underset{\text{(g)}}{\tfrac{1}{2}\text{Cl}_2} = \underset{\text{(c)}}{\text{NaCl}}$$

would be expected to take place with the evolution of heat, since an ionic solid is being formed. On the other hand a reaction such as:

$$\underset{\text{(c)}}{\text{NH}_4\text{Cl}} = \underset{\text{(g)}}{\text{NH}_3} + \underset{\text{(g)}}{\text{HCl}}$$

would be expected to occur with an absorption of energy since an ionic solid is being destroyed. Another example of the destruction of an ionic solid is the dissolution of the substance in water, and this process is most often accompanied by an absorption of heat though in some cases the hydration energy may be large enough to overcome this.

B. *Covalent bonds*

Nature of the bond

A covalent bond is formed when two neutral atoms approach each other in such a way that at a certain distance apart the potential energy of the

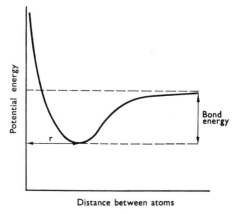

FIG. 21

system reaches a minimum. This happens because there occurs an over-lapping of atomic orbitals containing electrons of opposite spin which pair-up to give a region of common electron density to both atoms. This type of bond differs from the ionic bond in that it has a fixed direction in space, dependant on the way in which the atomic orbitals have combined together. Therefore whenever a covalent bond is formed in a system, the energy of the system becomes lower. This is illustrated in Fig. 21. (Compare with Fig. 18.)

In order to break the covalent bond when it has been formed energy must be put into the system and the amount of energy required to break any given bond therefore becomes a measure of the strength of the bond.

Bond energy

In order to compare the strengths of different covalent bonds, the term *bond energy* has been coined, and it is defined as the energy required to separate the constituent atoms of a given bond an infinite distance apart from each other in the gaseous state, under standard conditions, i.e. one atmosphere pressure and 25°C per mole of substance.

If we consider the case of the hydrogen molecule, the bond energy is equal in magnitude to the energy change for the reaction:

$$H_2 = H + H$$
$$\text{(g)} \quad \text{(g)} \quad \text{(g)}$$

In this case the bond energy of hydrogen is equal to the heat of dissociation of the molecule, and has a value of 104 kcal mole^{-1}. The bond energies for some of the common elements are given in Table 8. In the case of those elements which form multiple bonds the bond energies will be much greater than those which only contain a single bond. Note especially in this respect the high bond energy of the nitrogen molecule.

TABLE 8

Element	H_2	O_2	N_2	Cl_2	F_2
Bond energy kcal mole^{-1}	104	118	225	57·8	36·6

In the case of a compound such as methane four bonds must be ruptured according to the equation:

$$CH_4 = C + 4H$$
$$\text{(g)} \quad \text{(g)} \quad \text{(g)}$$

and this process is accompanied by the absorption of 398 kcal mole^{-1}. Since the four carbon–hydrogen bonds are equivalent we may assume that the energy required to rupture each of the carbon–hydrogen bonds is a quarter of the total energy required to dissociate the whole molecule. Thus the bond energy of the C—H bond will be $\frac{398}{4} = 99.5$ kcal mole^{-1}. A bond energy computed in such a way is known as an average bond energy. This method of calculation of bond energies takes no account of the fact that the dissociation:

$$CH_4 \quad = CH_3 \quad +H$$
$$(g) \qquad (g) \quad (g)$$

may not require exactly the same quantity of energy as the dissociation:

$$CH_3 \quad = CH_2 \quad +H$$
$$(g) \qquad (g) \quad (g)$$

When a specific bond is broken the energy required is known as the *bond dissociation energy*. For example, in the dissociation of one hydrogen atom from the methane molecule 104 kcal of energy per mole of methane is required. Thus we write $D(CH_3—H) = 104$ kcal mole^{-1}. In a similar way we can write $D(CH_2—H) = 106$ kcal, $D(CH—H) = 106$ kcal and $D(C—H) = 82$ kcal. It is important that the difference between the average bond energy and the dissociation bond energy is understood, especially if the reactivities of different species are being studied.

Again, the average bond energy of the oxygen–hydrogen bond from the reaction:

$$H_2O \quad = 2H \quad +O$$
$$(g) \qquad (g) \quad (g)$$

is 110·5 kcal per mole of O—H bonds.

However, the values for the two bond dissociation energies are $D(HO—H) = 118$ kcal, and $D(H—O) = 103$ kcal. The differences are appreciable and can be related to the fact that OH radicals are much more reactive than O atoms in combining with hydrogen atoms in more stable molecules.

Further extreme examples are provided by carbon dioxide, for which $D(OC—O) = 127$ kcal and $D(C—O) = 257$ kcal, and also nitrogen trioxide for which $D(O_2N—O) = 50$ kcal, $D(ON—O) = 72$ kcal and $D(O—N) = 151$ kcal. It must be realised that in order to attach any real meaning to the bond dissociation energies the structure of the molecule must be known, and also the products of the bond rupture. This is particularly relevant in the case where rearrangement of the atoms takes place after a given bond has been broken.

In the case of diatomic molecules the average bond energy will be the same as the bond dissociation energy, and for a molecule containing only two different atoms, for example CH_4, the average bond energy will be the same as the mean of the bond dissociation energies. The difference between the average bond energy and the bond dissociation energy arises because the fragments resulting from the dissociation are often different to the same group in the molecule, and therefore some kind of energy of reorganisation must be involved.

Zero-point energy

We have already seen how the potential energy of two atoms which constitute a covalent bond varies with the separation of the atoms in Fig. 21. The energy difference between the separated atoms at infinity and the atoms in the equilibrium position at a distance r apart was labelled loosely the 'bond energy'. However, the actual work required to separate the two species from each other completely is slightly less than this amount. For example, in Fig. 22 the work required to separate the species completely is given by AC not AB.

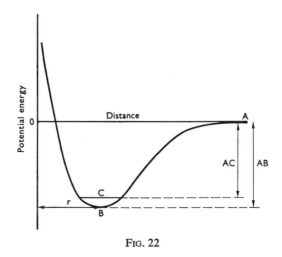

FIG. 22

This difference arises because the species which constitute the bond are not at rest relative to each other, but possess kinetic energy. This residual kinetic energy is known as the *zero-point energy*. The greater the mass of the species the lower the zero-point energy; for example for the H_2 molecule it amounts to 6·4 kcal mole^{-1} whereas for the D_2 molecule it is 4·5 kcal mole^{-1}, resulting in the fact that it is more difficult to dissociate D_2 than H_2.

Note that if for a given molecule the exact interatomic distances were known (values of r on the potential energy diagram) and the exact energy associated with the bonds were known, then Heisenberg's Uncertainty Principle would be violated, for this states that it is impossible to specify simultaneously the exact position and momentum of a particle because the instruments used to measure these quantities disturb the object being measured. Thus the zero-point energy is a measure of the energy which a molecule possesses even at the absolute zero of temperature.

Often discrepancies in the values for bond energies obtained from different sources are due, in part at least, to the fact that bond energies as measured (theoretically) at 0° A differ from those measured at 25° C by the heat energy required to raise the temperature of the system from 0° A to the standard one. The differences are usually of the order of 1 kcal mole^{-1}. It is conventional to state the magnitudes of bond energies at 25° C.

Constancy of bond energy

We have seen how the energy of a bond between two species in a molecule depends upon the nature and structure of the rest of the molecule in which the bond occurs, thus it was necessary to define bond dissociation energy rather than average bond energy. Hence, there is no strict justification for the assumption that the bond energy between two given species will remain constant throughout many compounds in which the bond occurs. Having said this it can now be pointed out that it is possible to derive average values of bond energies for a series of given bonds which do not vary too widely from compound to compound in which they occur. This has been done by Pauling, and some typical values of these bond energies are given in Table 9. Note, for example, that we took the average bond energy of the C—H bond in methane to be 99·5 kcal mole^{-1} but when taken over a wide selection of compounds this becomes 98·8 kcal mole^{-1}.

TABLE 9

Bond	Bond energy (kcal mole^{-1} at 25° C)	Bond	Bond energy (kcal mole^{-1} at 25° C)
C—H	98·8	H—F	135·0
C—Cl	78·5	H—Cl	103·0
C—C	80·0	H—Br	87·5
C=C	143·3	H—I	71·0
C≡C	194·4	C—F	121·0
C=O	179·0	P—H	77·0
C≡N	212·6	H—N	93·4
C—O	80·2	H—S	66·3
O—H	110·5	N=O	150·0
O—O	35·0	S=O	104·0
O—N	50·0	N—N	64·0
O—Cl	49·0	C—Br	68·0

Because the bond energies in Table 9 are not strictly bond dissociation energies but average values, we shall write them in a different way, viz. E(C—H)=98·8 kcal for the bond energy of the C—H bond.

Such values are useful from two standpoints; they can be used for the computation of other bond energies, and they can be used in the calculation of heat changes in chemical reactions. Examples of both will be given to illustrate these points.

Example

Calculate $E(C—C)$ for ethane, given the heat of formation of ethane to be $-20\cdot3$ kcal mole^{-1}, and the heats of dissociation of carbon and hydrogen to be $+171\cdot7$ and $+104$ kcal mole^{-1} respectively.

The formation of ethane may be represented by:

$$2C \quad\quad +3H_2 \quad = C_2H_6 \quad\quad\quad (1)$$
$$\text{(graphite)} \quad\text{(g)} \quad\quad \text{(g)}$$

In order to determine the total bond energy of ethane we must estimate the heat change for the reaction:

$$2C \quad +6H \quad = C_2H_6 \quad\quad\quad (2)$$
$$\text{(g)} \quad\quad \text{(g)} \quad\quad \text{(g)}$$

Since we are given

$$C \quad\quad\quad = C \quad\quad \Delta H = +171\cdot7 \text{ kcal}$$
$$\text{(graphite)} \quad \text{(g)}$$

and

$$H_2 \quad = 2H \quad\quad \Delta H = +104 \text{ kcal}$$
$$\text{(g)} \quad \text{(g)}$$

then by addition

$$2C \quad\quad\quad +3H_2 \quad = 2C \quad +6H \quad\quad\quad (3)$$
$$\text{(graphite)} \quad \text{(g)} \quad\quad \text{(g)}$$

is accompanied by a heat change of $2\times(+171\cdot7)+3\times(+104)$ kcal, i.e. $\Delta H = +655\cdot4$ kcal.

Now equation (2) may be obtained by the subtraction of equation (3) from equation (1), and therefore applying Hess's Law the reaction corresponding to equation (2) will be accompanied by a heat change of $-20\cdot3 -(+655\cdot4)$ kcal, i.e. $\Delta H = -675\cdot7$ kcal.

Therefore the total bond energy of ethane is $675\cdot7$ kcal mole^{-1}. Now in ethane there are six C—H bonds and one C—C bond; and therefore we have:

$$6\times E(C—H)+E(C—C) = 675\cdot7$$

Since

$$E(C—H) = 98\cdot8 \text{ kcal}$$
$$E(C—C) = 675\cdot7-6\times98\cdot8$$
$$= 675\cdot7-592\cdot8$$
$$= 82\cdot9 \text{ kcal mole}^{-1}$$

The bond energy of the C—C bond in ethane is therefore $82\cdot9$ kcal mole^{-1}.

Example

We are required to estimate the heat change for the reaction:

$$3CH_4 \quad = C_3H_8 \quad +2H_2$$
$$\text{(g)} \quad\quad \text{(g)} \quad\quad \text{(g)}$$

We can think of the reaction proceeding by the breaking of all the bonds in the reactant molecules and the forming of all the bonds in the product molecules from the individual gaseous atoms. That is we can simply add the total bond energies of the reactants and subtract this from the sum of the bond energies of the products.

The total bond energy of 3 moles of methane will be $12 \times E(\text{C—H})$ $= 12 \times 98 \cdot 8$ kcal (taking the average value for C—H) $= 1,185 \cdot 6$ kcal.

The bond energy of one mole of C_3H_8 will be $8 \times E(\text{C—H}) + 2 \times E(\text{C—C})$ $= 8 \times 98 \cdot 8 + (2 \times 80) = 950 \cdot 4$ kcal., while the bond energy of two moles of hydrogen $= 2 \times 104 = 208$ kcal.

Therefore in breaking the bonds in the reactant molecules $1,185 \cdot 6$ kcal of heat are absorbed, but in forming the bonds in the products $950 \cdot 4 + 208$ kcal of heat are evolved. Hence the above reaction will be accompanied by a heat change of $+ 1,185 \cdot 6 - (950 \cdot 4 + 208)$ kcal $= + 1,185 \cdot 6 - 1,158 \cdot 4 = + 27 \cdot 2$ kcal.

The reaction will therefore be an endothermic one, $\Delta H = + 27 \cdot 2$ kcal.

It can be seen from the above example how the use of bond energies enables us to estimate the heat changes for given chemical reactions. It will be obvious that if, during the reaction, very strong bonds are formed in the product molecules (e.g. nitrogen gas), then the chances are that the reaction will be exothermic. On the other hand if strong bonds in the reactant molecules are being destroyed then there is a likelihood of an endothermic reaction.

Factors affecting the magnitude of the bond energy

We have seen from the values of bond energies in the tables that covalent bonding is generally quite strong and certainly comparable with ionic bonding as measured by the lattice energies. We saw, in the case of ionic bonds, how different factors could affect the actual magnitude of the bond strength, and this will also be demonstrated for covalent bonding. In some cases these factors will have little effect on the magnitude of the bond energy but in others the effect may be so large as to modify the reactivity of the molecule considerably.

(i) Effect of bond length

The greater the bond length, as measured by the distance between the nuclei of the two atoms forming the bond, the lower the bond energy. This is illustrated in Table 10.

TABLE 10

Bond	H—H	F—F	Cl—Cl	Br—Br	I—I
Bond length Å	0·74	1·28	1·98	2·28	2·70
Bond energy kcal mole^{-1}	104	36·6	57·8	46·1	35·6

The tendency to greater bond energy with shorter bond length is probably due to the increased attraction of opposite charges at closer range. Larger atoms result in longer bonds but also have more electrons in the electron clouds which screen the effect of the increased charge on the nuclei, at the same time producing greater electron-cloud repulsions. The value of the bond energy for fluorine in the above table is unexpectedly small in view of what has been said. Compared with the other halogens we would expect the fluorine molecule to be the most stable of all. The low value of the bond energy has been attributed to the repulsion between the lone pairs of electrons on the fluorine atoms which is appreciable at small distances, but which is not so effective as the bond length increases. In contrast the bonds between fluorine and many other elements are quite strong, for example $E(C—F) = 121$ kcal and $E(C—Cl) = 78·5$ kcal (Table 9). Thus the fluorinated hydrocarbons are extremely resistant to attack.

(ii) Effect of bond polarity

When two different atoms participate in covalent bond formation there occurs an overlapping of atomic orbitals to give a region of common electron density between the two atoms. Because the two atoms are different their nuclei will have different forces of attraction for the shared electron pair, and therefore there will be an unequal sharing of the electrons between the two atoms. This means that the electrons will be closer to one of the atoms than the other and the covalent bond is said to have *polarity*. One of the atoms can therefore be considered to have a partial negative charge since the electron pair is situated much nearer to it than the other atom which has an equal but opposite positive charge. This is represented in Fig. 23.

$$A\cdot + \cdot B = (\overset{\delta+}{A} \quad \overset{\delta-}{:B})$$

Fig. 23

Because of this partial ionic character the bond between the two atoms will be strengthened, and the bond energy will therefore be greater than it would have been for a purely covalent bond between the same two atoms. Pauling made use of this difference in bond energy to formulate his scale of electronegativity values (these are a measure of the tendency which atoms have to attract electrons to themselves).

If we consider two atoms which form more than one compound we can compare the bond energy for each of these. Thus $E(P—Cl)$ in PCl_3 is 82·2 whereas in PCl_5 it is 66·7 kcal. Again, $E(Ti—Cl)$ in $TiCl_2$ is 141·5, in $TiCl_3$ it is 121·1 and in $TiCl_4$ it is 101·6 kcal.

The reason for the variations of bond energy is possibly that the more competitors there are for the electrons of a given atom the less negative charge each will acquire, and therefore the less polar the bond. Thus the partial negative charge on the chlorine atoms in the examples quoted decreases with the number of chlorines per molecule, and hence the lower the bond energy.

When one of the atoms is hydrogen and the other is a highly electronegative element then the polarity of the bond is quite marked and the bond energy is therefore relatively high. Consult Table 9 for the bond energies of HF, HCl and H—O for example.

(iii) Unsaturated character of the bond

It can be seen by inspection of the bond energies in Table 9 that those atoms which are joined by a double or triple bond have much greater values than the corresponding single bonds. This is not surprising for there are effectively two or three bonds where there was previously only one. However it will also be noticed that the gain in bond energy from the introduction of a second bond between the two atoms is not necessarily equal to the first bond energy. An example should make this clear.

The bond energy values for the carbon–carbon bond in ethane, ethylene and acetylene are 80·0, 143·3 and 194·4 kcal mole^{-1} respectively. This implies that the second bond between the carbon atoms is formed with the evolution of only 63·3 kcal mole^{-1} and the third bond with the evolution of 51·1 kcal mole^{-1}. This means that acetylene will be more reactive than ethylene because less energy is needed to rupture a bond between the carbon atoms. Ethylene will in turn be more reactive than ethane for the same reason. The differences arise because of the way in which the bonds are formed. Thus the first bond between the carbon atoms is formed by an overlap of the atomic orbitals as illustrated in Fig. 24(a). Such a bond is known as a sigma bond (σ bond). The second bond arises from an overlap of atomic orbitals in the way illustrated in Fig. 24(b). This is known as a pi bond (π bond).

(a) σ bond   (b) π bond

FIG. 24

Thus the π bond has a lower bond energy than the σ bond, and it is important that we realise they are two distinct types. The third bond in the acetylene molecule is another π bond but it has even less energy since it is undergoing some strain in being forced into close proximity of the other two bonds already present.

(iv) Effect of percentage of s character in the bond

The carbon–hydrogen bond in the hydrocarbons differs in character according to the hybridisation of the orbitals present. The table below shows that the greater the percentage of s orbital in the hybridised bond the greater the bond energy.

TABLE 11

Compound	Hybridisation	Percentage s character in the bond	E(C—H) (kcal mole^{-1})
CH_4	sp^3	25%	99·5
C_2H_4	sp^2	33%	105·5
C_2H_2	sp	50%	120·6

(v) *Effect of resonance*

The acetate ion CH_3COO^- might be written in the forms:

$$CH_3.C\diagup^{O^-}_{\diagdown O} \quad \text{and} \quad CH_3.C\diagup^{O}_{\diagdown O^-}$$

These forms are not the same but they have the same energy. Now the bond length of the carbon–oxygen bonds in the acetate ion is the same in each case, implying that the two bonds are equivalent and not one single and one double bond. This means that the double bond in either of the forms above has become distributed partially between both bonds, resulting in neither of the bonds being single or double but something in between. Such a situation is known as *resonance*. This is a common occurrence for molecules in which a double bond might possibly be in one of two places but not in both at the same time. The resonant forms have no existence independently at any time and so the concept is quite different from that of tautomerism where an equilibrium is set up between the two forms.

Now when resonance takes place the actual structure of a compound is more stable than any of the several resonant forms. This is illustrated in Fig. 25.

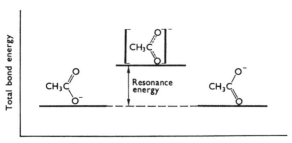

FIG. 25

The difference between the energy of the most stable resonant form and the actual structure is known as the *resonance energy*.

The resonance energy can often make quite a significant difference in the total bond energy of a compound, and because of this great stability is sometimes conferred on a compound which otherwise would have been thought to be unstable. The value of the resonance energy may be estimated in the following way.

The measured heat of formation of carbon dioxide from the gaseous atoms is 383 kcal mole^{-1}, and this is therefore equal to the actual total bond energy. Now from Table 9 $E(C{=}O) = 179$ kcal and therefore assuming the structure $O{=}C{=}O$ the total bond energy expected would be 358 kcal. The difference, 25 kcal mole^{-1} is the resonance energy. This arises from the participation of such resonant forms as those shown in Fig. 26.

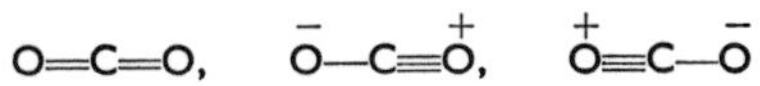

$$O{=}C{=}O, \quad \overset{-}{O}{-}C{\equiv}\overset{+}{O}, \quad \overset{+}{O}{\equiv}C{-}\overset{-}{O}$$

FIG. 26

Perhaps one of the best-known cases of resonance is that of the benzene molecule. Kekulé proposed the structure (I) for benzene (Fig. 27).

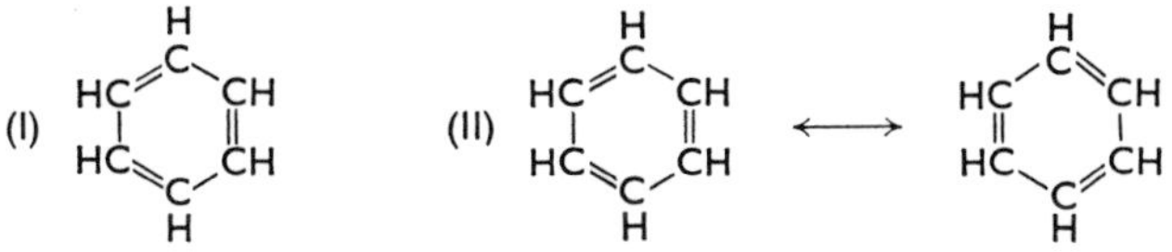

FIG. 27

Now the total bond energy of the Kekulé structure is about 40 kcal less than the observed heat of formation of benzene from the gaseous atoms. Thus the resonance energy for benzene is 40 kcal mole^{-1}, this being due to the participation of resonance such as that in Fig. 27 (II).

Thus whenever resonance can occur for a given molecule greater stability is conferred and the energy liberated on the formation of the molecule is greater than it otherwise would have been.

C. *Coordinate bonds*

Coordinate bonds are similar to covalent bonds in that a sharing of electrons between two atoms takes place by an overlap of atomic orbitals. However, in the case of coordinate bonds both electrons originate from the same atom. Thus before coordinate bond formation can take place there must be some species which possesses a lone pair of electrons and another species which is electronically deficient. For example, the ammonia molecule which has a lone pair of electrons can donate this to a molecule such as boron trifluoride, which is electronically deficient, to form the well-known addition compound:

$$
\begin{array}{ccc}
\text{H} \quad \text{F} & & \text{H} \quad \text{F} \\
| \quad | & & | \quad | \\
\text{H—N:} + \text{B—F} = & \text{H—N} \rightarrow \text{B—F} \\
| \quad | & & | \quad | \\
\text{H} \quad \text{F} & & \text{H} \quad \text{F}
\end{array}
$$

The arrow indicates a coordinate bond and points towards the species receiving the electron pair. Such bonds are formed particularly by the transition element ions with molecules possessing lone pairs (ammonia, water for example) or with other ions having lone pairs (the halide ions).

It is our purpose at present to discuss the relative strengths of different bond types and therefore we shall not include any account of crystal field theory in connection with the formation of coordinate bonds. Suffice it to say that the bond energies are of the same order as those of covalent bonds as would be expected from the nature of the bond. There are variations in bond energy due mainly to the ease with which the donor species is willing to part with the lone pair, and the readiness with which the electrons are accepted. Factors which will influence these processes are the partial charge on the atoms, the types of group to which they are attached and the orbitals which are available for bonding.

D. *Metallic bonds*

The structure of a metallic element is made up of a lattice of cations between which the electrons from the outermost orbitals of the atoms are relatively free to move, so accounting for the electrical conductivity of the metal. The moving electron cloud confers great stability on the crystal and the lattice energy is correspondingly quite large. The great mechanical strength of many of the metals used in engineering bears witness to the fact that the forces between the atoms in the crystal must be quite large.

A measure of the lattice energy can be obtained by a consideration of the heats of atomisation of the metal; that is, the heat change associated with the process:

$$
M_{(c)} = M_{(g)}
$$

and some typical values are given in Table 12.

It will be seen that the transition metals generally have higher heats of atomisation than the main group metals, and this may be due to the greater part that the d orbitals play in forming stronger bonds in the case of the transition metals. Certainly the more bonding electrons there are available the stronger the metallic bonding. (As with covalent bonds where the more shared electron pairs the stronger the bonding.)

TABLE 12

Metal	Heat of atomisation (kcal per mole of atoms)	Metal	Heat of atomisation (kcal per mole of atoms)
W	+201·6	Li	+37·1
Ti	+112·4	Na	+25·9
Fe	+96·7	K	+21·4
Cu	+81·5	Zn	+31·2

As might be expected the strength of the metallic bond decreases as the atomic radius of the metal increases; this is seen in the values given for the alkali metals. The reason is probably the same as for covalent bonding, that is as the radius increases there is a greater shielding of the nuclear charge by the electron cloud.

The values in Table 12 therefore indicate that if during a chemical reaction a solid metal is either formed or destroyed then there will be a correspondingly large change in energy, certainly comparable with energy changes due to the formation and rupture of ionic and covalent bonds.

E. *Hydrogen bonds*

When a hydrogen atom is bonded to an electronegative atom the influence which the electronegative element exerts on the shared pair of electrons polarises the bond leaving an effective positive charge on the hydrogen atom; for example:

$$\overset{\delta_+}{H}—\overset{\delta_-}{X}$$

Because the hydrogen atom has no electron cloud to shield this effective positive charge there is an attraction between the hydrogen atom and the electronegative atom of another molecule:

$$---\overset{\delta_+}{H}—\overset{\delta_-}{X}---\overset{\delta_+}{H}—\overset{\delta_-}{X}---\overset{\delta_+}{H}—\overset{\delta_-}{X}---$$

The attraction is primarily electrostatic in nature, and takes place when the hydrogen atom is bonded only to the most electronegative elements, such as fluorine, oxygen, nitrogen and chlorine. As the electronegativity of the element decreases so does the strength of the *hydrogen bond* as it is called. The hydrogen bond is weak compared to ionic or covalent bonds being of the order of 5 kcal mole^{-1}. For the hydrogen–fluorine bond the value is 6·7 kcal, hydrogen–oxygen it is 4·5 kcal and for hydrogen–nitrogen it is 1·3 kcal. This is reflected in the ease with which hydrogen bonds are formed, and therefore they are quite readily ruptured. Thus, if during a chemical reaction hydrogen bonds are either formed or ruptured the heat change due to this alone is not likely to be very great.

Hydrogen bonding occurs in such compounds as water, hydrogen fluoride and ammonia, resulting in anomalously high boiling points for these compounds compared to the other hydrides in their respective groups. Hydrogen bonding among organic compounds is particularly common, especially with carboxylic acids in non-polar solents (see later).

F. *Other types of bond*

Among the other bond types not already mentioned is the so-called van der Waals forces. This type of attraction is thought to arise from electronic interactions in the molecules of the compounds concerned, possibly because of fluctuating dipole moments. The forces only become important when the molecules are in close proximity, for their effect falls off rapidly with distance. The magnitude of the strength of such bonds is of the order of 1 kcal mole^{-1}, and hence they will have little contribution to make to the overall energy change occurring during chemical reaction.

There are other weaker attractions between different species, such as the dipole–dipole and ion–dipole interactions, but these are of still weaker energy that they are of no relevance to our present discussion.

Summary

It is the change in the bond strengths during a chemical reaction which determines the heat change for that reaction. If the bonds involved are strong ones, ionic, covalent or metallic, and the process results in the net formation or rupture of such bonds, then the heat change may be quite large. If the only effective change taking place is that due to weaker bonds, hydrogen bonds for example, then the heat change may be very small. Estimates of the magnitudes of such changes may be made by the use of tables of bond energies and lattice energies which are available for a wide variety of elements and compounds.

Part Three
Entropy Changes in Chemical Reactions

5 Sources of Entropy Changes

Entropy and probability

In Chapter 1 we saw that the 'entropy' of a system can be taken as an indication of the degree of orderliness of that system. When applied to chemical reaction we decided that this could be interpreted in terms of the structures of the substances involved in the reaction (page 9). In what follows we shall examine the connection between entropy and order more closely and attempt to discover any generalisations by which we can make intelligent guesses at the sign and relative magnitude of entropy changes in given reactions.

Now we have already seen that during spontaneous change a system tends to become more disordered, and it is obvious that a condition of disorder is more likely to be established than a completely ordered state (shuffle a pack of cards several times to convince yourself!). Thus entropy and probability must be linked together in some way. Entropy is an extensive property, and therefore if two independent systems have entropies S_1 and S_2 the total entropy will be $(S_1 + S_2)$. Probability, on the other hand, is a multiplicative property in the sense that if the two systems mentioned have probabilities W_1 and W_2, the total probability of both considered together is $W_1 \times W_2$.

Hence the connection between the entropy S and the probability W must be of the form:

$$S \propto \log W$$

In fact, the relationship has been expressed as:

$$S = k \log_e W$$

where k is the Boltzmann constant. This equation has become the basis for modern statistical thermodynamics. Note that at the absolute zero of temperature, when most simple substances go into a crystalline state, i.e. a state of very high, if not complete, order, the entropy of the crystal will be given by:

$$S° = k \cdot \log_e 1$$
$$= 0$$

since the probability is unity. This will give us a basis for the measurement of entropy later.

The task of deciding in advance which of several given structures is the more probable is not always a simple one, indeed in many cases it is almost impossible. But in spite of this there still remain many general types of reaction for which it is possible to predict the sign of the entropy change, and these will be studied in what follows.

Reactions in which there is a change of state

As is well known, the solid state is essentially one in which the constituent atoms of the substance are closely packed together and thus occupy relatively fixed positions in space. The regular arrangement of the atoms on a crystal lattice can be confirmed by X-ray diffraction data. Now since the atoms are close-packed and are relatively restricted in movement the overall structure of a solid tends to be quite highly ordered. No solid has a perfectly ordered structure, for above absolute zero of temperature the atoms are vibrating about mean positions on the crystal lattice and in this sense no atom may be assigned a definite position in space. Thus the structure can never be known *exactly* and cannot therefore have perfect order. The case of the crystal *at* absolute zero has already been mentioned. The regularity of the solid structure of some common substances is illustrated in Fig. 28, below:

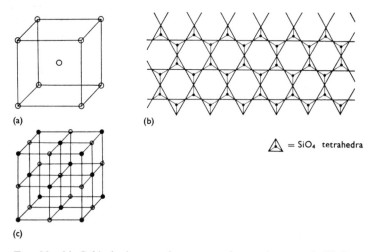

(a)

(b)

△ = SiO₄ tetrahedra

(c)

FIG. 28 (a) Cubic body-centred structure of potassium metal; (b) Open sheet structure of the micas; (c) Octahedral structure of common salt.

Although only three examples of solid-state structures have been shown the student can confirm the high degree of order associated with this state by reference to the many structures illustrated in chemistry textbooks.

The liquid state is one in which fairly strong attraction is retained between the atoms or molecules, but in which any regularity in structure is confined to only a few molecular diameters.

The gaseous state is characterised by very little intermolecular attraction and the molecules are therefore almost independent of each other. It naturally follows that in such a state there will be little regularity of structure.

Therefore in passing from the solid state to the liquid state, and also from the liquid to the gaseous state there will be an increase in entropy of the substance, since each of these processes is accompanied by a loss of regularity in structure. Also, within any given state, the effect of raising the temperature will be to increase the entropy of the substance, for in raising the temperature the kinetic energy of the atoms will be increased so making the position of any given atom more uncertain. It will be appreciated that the increase in entropy within a given state will in general be smaller than that due to change of state. The effect of temperature on the entropy of a substance may be illustrated graphically (Fig. 29):

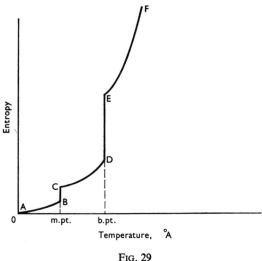

FIG. 29

No attempt has been made to draw the graph to scale, but it can be seen that the curve begins at the origin and the part AB represents the entropy increase as the temperature of the solid is raised from absolute zero to the melting point. During the melting process there is an increase in entropy as the substance changes from all solid at B to all liquid at C. The part CD represents the increase in entropy of the liquid phase as the temperature is taken to the boiling point. Here there is a large increase in entropy (much larger than that during melting) as the liquid boils and becomes gaseous, after which the entropy of the gas continues to increase with increasing temperature. At very high temperatures no atomic aggregates will exist and only sub-atomic particles will be present — this will, of course, correspond to a state of high entropy. The temperature at which this would happen has been estimated at $100,000°$ A.

Because of the difference in intermolecular attraction between the three states, the entropy of vaporisation is usually much greater than the entropy of melting for a given substance. In fact, for many liquids the value of the entropy of vaporisation is approximately the same, about 23 entropy units (e.u.), where 1 e.u. = 1 cal. $°A^{-1}$ mole^{-1}. The values of entropy of vaporisation of some liquids are given in Table 13.

The reason for the relatively high values for some liquids (water and ethanol for example), is that in such liquids association occurs via hydrogen bonding. Thus the arrangement of the molecules is much more ordered than it otherwise would have been and consequently has a lower entropy value. Hence for such substances the entropy of vaporisation will be greater than 23 e.u.

TABLE 13

Substance in the liquid state	Entropy of vaporisation (e.u.)
Benzene	21·2
Propyl acetate	22·2
Mercury	22·6
Zinc	23·5
Potassium chloride	24·0
Water	26·0
Ethyl alcohol	26·7

It follows from what has been discussed above that if, during a chemical reaction, a gas is produced from reactants which were in the liquid, or even solid state then the entropy change for that reaction will tend to be quite large and positive. Alternatively, if more gas molecules are present in the products than in the reactants, then there would again be an increase of entropy. For example the reaction:

$$Zn + 2HCl = ZnCl_2 + H_2$$
$$\text{(c)} \quad \text{(aq)} \quad \text{(aq)} \quad \text{(g)}$$

would be accompanied by an increase in entropy, as would the reaction:

$$2C + O_2 = 2CO$$
$$\text{(graphite)} \quad \text{(g)} \quad \text{(g)}$$

On the other hand, examples of reactions accompanied by a decrease in entropy are:

$$N_2 + 3H_2 = 2NH_3$$
$$\text{(g)} \quad \text{(g)} \quad \text{(g)}$$

and,

$$2H_2 + O_2 = 2H_2O$$
$$\text{(g)} \quad \text{(g)} \quad \text{(l)}$$

We can also readily appreciate that for those substances which sublime there will be a fairly large increase in entropy as the change from the solid to the gaseous state takes place directly. Among such substances are iodine, naphthalene and benzoic acid.

Although not strictly a change of state, the process of dissolution of solids in liquids will generally involve an increase in entropy. During this process the atoms or ions leave their positions on the crystal lattice and become relatively less ordered in the solvent. Thus the entropy change is positive. It is of interest to note that in those cases where solvation takes place (hydration in the case of water as solvent) the entropy increase will not be so large as it would otherwise have been. The same general considerations apply to solutions of liquids in liquids, and to the diffusion of gases (already discussed). Whenever a gas is dissolved in a liquid there will, of course, be a decrease in entropy, and vice versa when the gas is released from solution (the soda siphon).

The student may consider for himself the differences in entropy which occur, for example, between an amorphous solid and a crystalline one, or between two allotropes of the same element.

Reactions in which simple species are produced from more complex ones, and vice versa

Thermal dissociation

This is probably the most obvious type of reaction in which simple species are produced from more complex ones. For example, vapour density measurements indicate that at 200° C aluminium chloride consists mainly of Al_2Cl_6 molecules, whereas at 800° C the vapour is almost entirely composed of $AlCl_3$ molecules. The change from the dimer to the monomer is one which must necessarily involve an increase in entropy, for the dimer is the more highly organised molecule (see Fig. 30). Ferric chloride behaves in a similar manner.

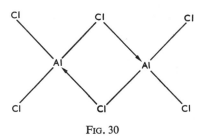

Fig. 30

The dissociation of ammonium chloride may be cited as a further example of this type of change. Here the change is from a solid to two different gases, and the resultant increase in entropy in this case must be quite large.

$$NH_4Cl \underset{(c)}{} = NH_3 \underset{(g)}{} + HCl \underset{(g)}{}$$

Elements also undergo this type of reaction. Probably the most familiar example is that of sulphur:

$$S_8 = 4S_2 = 8S$$

Just above the boiling-point the vapour consists of S_8 molecules (the structure of which is that of a puckered ring, as illustrated in Fig. 31), but

6

as the temperature is raised the vapour density decreases indicating the formation of diatomic then monatomic molecules. Once again the student may consult a textbook for further illustrations of the dissociation of elements; for example the halogens, phosphorus and selenium.

Association

In the same way that thermal dissociation is accompanied by increase in entropy, it follows that association will be accompanied by a decrease in entropy. Thus it is well known that in solution and in the gas phase many substances are associated, for example carboxylic acids in non-polar solvents where the association is promoted by the formation of hydrogen bonds (Fig. 32).

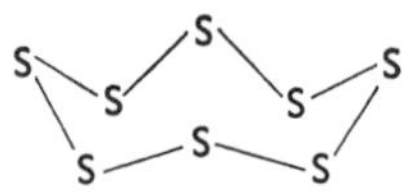

FIG. 31 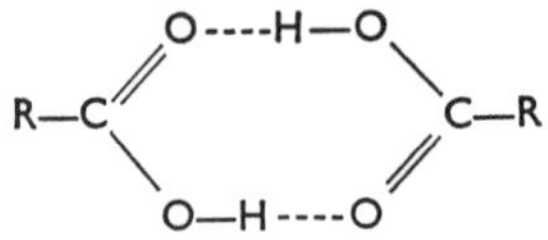   FIG. 32

Hydrogen fluoride, water and ammonia provide additional examples of association for the student to consult.

Polymerisation reactions

These are probably the most common types of reaction which illustrate the change in entropy accompanying change in molecular structure. The polymer is the more ordered arrangement and will therefore be formed with a decrease in entropy. For example the polymerisation of acetylene to benzene at 400° C:

$$3C_2H_2 = C_6H_6$$

or the polymerisation of ethylene, at 200° C, under pressure with a catalyst:

$$H_2C{=}CH_2 + H_2C{=}CH_2 + H_2C{=}CH_2 + \ldots$$
$$= \ldots -CH_2-CH_2-CH_2-CH_2-CH_2-CH_2-\ldots$$

Formation of coordination complexes

One of the outstanding features of transition element ions is the ability to form complexes with suitable coordinating agents. Since the condition of the complex ion is one of much greater order than that of the simpler species from which it is produced, the reaction must take place with a decrease in entropy.

$$Cu^{2+} + 4NH_3 = Cu(NH_3)_4^{2+}$$

Enough examples have been given to illustrate the changes in entropy accompanying changes in structure of reactants and products, and the student may care to satisfy himself further by a consideration of organic addition reactions or even radioactive decay.

Effect of mass on the entropy of gases

On examination of Table 14 below it will be seen that compounds of elements of higher atomic weight tend to have higher entropies. The entropy values given in the table are the Standard Molar Entropies.

TABLE 14

Gas	S_m° (e.u.)	Gas	S_m° (e.u.)	Gas	S_m° (e.u.)
Hydrogen fluoride	41·5	Helium	30·1	Hydrogen	31·2
Hydrogen chloride	44·6	Neon	34·95	Deuterium	34·4
Hydrogen bromide	47·5	Argon	37·0	Nitrogen	45·8
Hydrogen iodide	49·4			Oxygen	49·0

Within the series of hydrogen halides, or the rare gases, the effect of increase in mass is to produce increase of entropy. The reason for this presumably lies in the distribution and spacing of the available energy levels

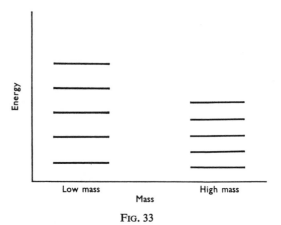

FIG. 33

in the compound. A full treatment is beyond the scope of this monograph, but it may be simplified as follows. It can be shown that the spacings of the energy levels within a given atom of gas are inversely proportional to the mass of the atom; i.e. the greater the atomic weight the closer the energy levels (illustrated in Fig. 33).

Now if the energy levels are closer together the total energy of the gas may be distributed in many more ways than if the energy levels are far apart. Thus the probability of the gas will be greater, and from the equation $S = k . \log_e W$ the entropy will also be greater.

It will also be noticed that the standard molar entropy for nitrogen, which is lighter (28·016) than argon (39·944), is greater than that of argon. The reason for this is that in the monatomic gas only translational energy levels are available and these are spaced relatively far apart, whereas in the diatomic gas there are rotational and possibly vibrational energy levels available and these are much closer to each other. Therefore the probability is higher for the diatomic gas and the entropy is greater.

Thus the reaction:

$$\text{AlBr}_3 \quad + \text{PCl}_3 \quad = \text{AlCl}_3 \quad + \text{PBr}_3$$
$$\text{(c)} \qquad \text{(g)} \qquad \text{(c)} \qquad \text{(g)}$$

will be accompanied by an increase in entropy, although in magnitude this may be small. In any reaction in which the energy may be distributed in a larger number of ways in the products than in the reactants there will be an increase in entropy.

Increase in mass has the same effect on the entropy of crystalline substances, i.e. the greater the mass the greater the entropy. (See Table 15.)

TABLE 15

Crystalline substance	NaF	KF	PbO	PbS
Standard molar entropy (S_m° e.u.)	14·0	15·9	16·2	21·8

Summary

The change in entropy accompanying a chemical reaction may be estimated, qualitatively at least, by a consideration of the structures of the species taking part in the reaction, since entropy and probability are related by the equation $S = k . \log_e W$. If during the reaction a significant change in state occurs, or if a marked change in the complexity of the species takes place, then an approximate estimation of the magnitude of that entropy change can be made.

Thus, together with the estimate of ΔH, the ΔS obtained above, although only approximate, will enable us to decide the sign, at least, of the free energy change ΔG via the equation $\Delta G = \Delta H - T . \Delta S$. It is important to realise that although ΔH values are often of the order of ten *kilocalories* entropy changes are of the order of a few entropy units (*calories* per degree). Therefore at ordinary temperatures, when T is about 300° A, the term $T . \Delta S$ will only have magnitude of the order of one kilocalorie. Hence at ordinary temperatures entropy changes are usually small enough to have little effect on the direction of spontaneous reaction, although the influence of the entropy change will increase with increasing temperature.

6 Entropy as a Thermodynamic Function

Thermodynamics and thermodynamic functions

Thermodynamics is essentially a study of the various energy changes which a given system experiences when it changes from one state to another. When the system is a chemical reaction, as in the cases we shall be considering, the study is known as *chemical thermodynamics*. Such a study will provide no information about the rate at which the system moves from the initial to the final state, nor about the mechanism of the change; we have already seen this to be the province of reaction kinetics. Thus, unless it is quite clearly defined, thermo*dynamics* is a term which can lead to a certain amount of confusion.

A thermodynamic function may therefore be defined as one which has a fixed value for a given state of the system which does not depend on the way in which that state has been attained. We have already seen how the change in heat energy during a chemical reaction conforms to this definition as expressed in Hess's Law. Other thermodynamic functions which we shall use are entropy and free energy.

It is worthwhile noting here the difference in the two main methods of approach to the study of chemical change. The kinetic theory approach involves the study of the behaviour of the individual atoms and molecules in the reaction, and from this is inferred the behaviour of a large number of such particles. In the thermodynamic approach experiments and observations are made on the bulk properties of matter, which does not involve any assumptions concerning the nature of the individual particles constituting the system.

Extensive and intensive properties

Properties whose magnitude depends upon the quantity of matter present in the system are said to be extensive properties. In addition to heat content and volume, as two obvious examples, entropy may also be classed under this heading. Those properties which are independent of the quantity of material present are known as intensive properties, and will include temperature, density, vapour pressure and refractive index.

Reversible and irreversible processes

In thermodynamics the words 'reversible' and 'irreversible' have come to have rather a special meaning, and before we proceed any further we should understand what we mean when we refer to these terms.

Essentially, a reversible process is one which is carried out infinitesimally slowly so that the system is at all times in equilibrium with its own surroundings. This implies that during the process neither the temperature nor the pressure must alter from its equilibrium value. An irreversible process is therefore one in which the system does not remain in equilibrium with its surroundings throughout.

An illustration of the difference between a reversible and irreversible way of carrying out the same process is seen in the expansion of a gas. If the gas is allowed to expand suddenly, by moving back a piston quickly, then the temperature of the gas will fall and an irreversible expansion will have taken place. If the piston is moved so slowly that at all times the pressure on both sides of it remains the same then a reversible change will have been achieved.

It is obvious that a reversible change can never be achieved in practice for it would take an infinite time to complete, whereas an irreversible change may take only a short time. Now the spontaneous reactions to which we have been referring in the earlier chapters take a very short time to complete, and therefore it must follow that all spontaneous processes are irreversible, a statement made on page 4. Although it must be impossible to attain a completely reversible change in practice an approach towards reversibility may be made in some cases. We shall see later how this can happen in the case where the reaction is carried out in a cell so that electrical energy is released and an e.m.f. set up. If the e.m.f. of the cell is balanced against the potential difference down a potentiometer wire no current flows through the cell and reversible conditions are established. This will be made use of in the measurement of entropy and free energy changes.

We may therefore say that any conditions for reversibility are also conditions for equilibrium, and any conditions for irreversibility are conditions for spontaneous change.

Concept of entropy

The concept of entropy was first introduced in connection with the theory of heat engines, and as such became very important to engineers. It is probably because of this that chemistry students have often fought shy of any attempt that has been made to introduce the concept into a chemistry course. Probably the greatest contribution made in the development of the concept of entropy was by Carnot, whose considerations of the performance of an ideal heat engine, in which all changes were carried out reversibly, paved the way for a quantitative treatment of the concept. We shall not be concerned here with a detailed description of Carnot's work, for it is only of interest to the chemist from a historical standpoint, and it is the author's contention that much of the confusion in students' minds over the study of thermodynamics is due to an almost impossible attempt to relate directly what happens during a chemical reaction to the performance of an ideal heat engine. Thus we shall accept the conclusions which Carnot arrived at and use them in considering chemical change, but at the same time acknowledge that the work done in connection with heat engines was of fundamental importance.

For any reversible process in which a minute quantity of heat dq is absorbed at a temperature $T°A$, the increase in entropy dS is given by:

$$dS = \frac{dq}{T}$$

For an irreversible (i.e. spontaneous) process:

$$dS > \frac{dq}{T}$$

and these are the types of reaction that we shall be considering.

For finite changes in entropy ΔS we must integrate the above equation:

$$\Delta S = \int_{T_1}^{T_2} dS = \int_{T_1}^{T_2} \frac{dq}{T}$$

between the temperature limits T_2 and T_1. In order for the above equality to hold it must be stressed that the heat change dq must be measured under reversible conditions.

It follows that for an adiabatic change, i.e. one in which no heat enters or leaves the system, $dq=0$ and consequently there can be no change in entropy. Such changes have therefore been referred to as *isentropic* changes.

Units of entropy

Since the change in entropy as defined above involves a heat change divided by a temperature, the units of entropy are calories degree^{-1}, and this is often known as 'entropy units' where 1 e.u. $= 1$ calorie degree^{-1}.

Second Law of Thermodynamics

The definition of the entropy change just outlined may be regarded as one expression of what is known as the second law of thermodynamics. We saw how there were many alternative ways of expressing the first law, and this is so with the second one. Because of the way in which the concept of entropy was introduced many of the first expressions were in terms of the performance of heat engines, but from the chemist's point of view the second law may be stated thus: the total amount of entropy in nature is increasing.

The second law as stated above will only apply to a system which contains a large enough number of molecules, and if applied to a system containing only a few molecules it is possible that it would fail.

Entropy changes for an ideal gas

Consider the supply of a quantity of heat dq to one mole of an ideal gas. This heat will be used for two purposes; to increase the temperature of the gas at constant volume and to expand the gas. Therefore we can write:

$$dq = C_v.dT + P.dV$$

where dT is the small increase in temperature, P is the pressure of the gas and dV is the small increase in volume. Now if the heat change takes place under reversible conditions the entropy change for the process at a temperature $T°$A will be given by:

$$dS = \frac{dq}{T} = \frac{C_v.dT}{T} + \frac{P.dV}{T}$$

For an ideal gas $P.V = RT$ and therefore $P = RT/V$.

Thus
$$dS = \frac{C_v.dT}{T} + \frac{RT.dV}{T.V}$$

For a finite change in entropy we may therefore write:

$$\Delta S = \int_{T_1}^{T_2} dS = \int_{T_1}^{T_2} \frac{C_v.dT}{T} + \int_{V_1}^{V_2} \frac{R.dV}{V}$$

Assuming C_v to be independent of temperature over the range considered (see page 27) this becomes:

$$\Delta S = C_v.\log_e \frac{T_2}{T_1} + R.\log_e \frac{V_2}{V_1}$$

At constant temperature the first term on the right-hand side of the last equation would vanish and the change in entropy would then be given by:

$$\Delta S = R.\log_e \frac{V_2}{V_1}$$

or alternatively since PV is constant for an ideal gas

$$\Delta S = R.\log_e \frac{P_1}{P_2}$$

This is in accordance with the qualitative ideas outlined in the previous chapter, where an increase in volume led to an increase in entropy.

At constant pressure, however, the entropy change for an ideal gas becomes:

$$\Delta S = C_p.\log_e \frac{T_2}{T_1}$$

which once again is in accordance with the qualitative ideas of entropy changes already outlined.

Since entropy is an extensive property then the entropy change for n moles of gas will be n times greater than in the equations above.

Entropy changes for changes in state

The processes of melting and boiling are reversible ones for at all times the system is in equilibrium with its surroundings, pressure and temperature remaining constant. Thus it is quite a simple matter to formulate the entropy changes accompanying these processes. If the molar latent heat of fusion of the substance is L_f then the change in entropy during the melting is given by:

$$\Delta S = \frac{L_f}{T_m} \text{ mole}^{-1}$$

where T_m is the melting point of the substance in °A. In a similar way the molar entropy of vaporisation is given by:

$$\Delta S = \frac{L_v}{T_b}$$

Since heat must be supplied to melt a solid or vapourise a liquid, and since both T_m and T_b must always be positive, the entropy changes must also be positive, i.e. there will be an increase in entropy.

Some values of the entropy of vaporisation of a few liquids are given in Table 13 on page 64.

As an illustration of the application of the principles outlined above the following example is included.

Example

Calculate the entropy change which takes place when one mole of ice at 0° C is converted to steam at one atmosphere pressure at 100° C.

Heat must be supplied in order to bring about three separate changes in the above process. Firstly the ice must be converted to water at 0° C; secondly the water at 0° C must be raised in temperature to 100° C; and lastly the water at 100° C must be converted to steam at the same temperature and pressure. All of these stages involve an increase in entropy and the total increase in entropy is therefore the sum of them. Thus, the entropy change will be given by:

$$\Delta S = \frac{L_f}{T_m} + C_p . \log_e \frac{T_2}{T_1} + \frac{L_v}{T_b}$$

Substituting the appropriate values for water, we have

$$\Delta S = \frac{1,436}{273} + 18 . \log_e \frac{373}{273} + \frac{9,720}{373} \text{ e.u.}$$

$$= 5 \cdot 26 + 5 \cdot 62 + 26 \cdot 06 \text{ e.u.}$$

$$= 36 \cdot 94 \text{ e.u.}$$

It will be seen from the above example that the greatest entropy change of all takes place during the vaporisation process, and this was predicted qualitatively in the previous chapter.

74

Entropy changes for real substances

We have so far considered entropy changes for gases, solids and liquids which behave ideally. If we would calculate entropy changes for processes involving real substances then we must make some allowance for the non-ideality. This can be done most conveniently by expressing the variation of the heat capacity with temperature, as shown on page 27, in the equation for the entropy change, and integrating between the temperature limits concerned,

i.e.
$$\Delta S = \int_{T_1}^{T_2} \frac{C_p}{T} \cdot dT = \int_{T_1}^{T_2} \frac{(a + bT + cT^2 + \ldots)}{T} \cdot dT$$

This integral may be evaluated either mathematically, if the form of the equation for the variation of the heat capacity of the substance with temperature is known, or experimentally by determining the values of the heat capacity at several temperatures within the limits of the integration. In this case it is most convenient to plot a graph of C_p/T against T, when the entropy change will be given by the area under the curve between the two temperature limits, see Fig. 34.

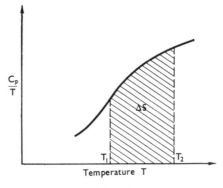

Fig. 34

Absolute entropy values

We have only considered the evaluation of entropy changes so far, and if we are to attempt to determine the absolute entropy of a given substance at a stated temperature then we must obviously adopt a reference standard. It has already been stated, in Chapter 5, page 61, that the entropy of all crystalline substances at absolute zero of temperature is taken as zero. This last statement has become known as the *Third Law of Thermodynamics*.

This law follows from the suggestions which Nernst made in connection with the variation of the heat capacity of different substances with temperature, among which the most relevant to the present discussion being that

the heat capacities of solids tends to zero at the absolute zero of temperature. Experiment confirmed these suggestions. Hence, from the equation:

$$\Delta S = \int_0^T \frac{C_p}{T} \cdot dT$$

since the limits of integration are $0°$ A and $T°$ A, and since C_p must be
positive or zero, then ΔS must also be positive or zero. Thus the lowest
possible entropy value a substance can have is at the absolute zero of
temperature. As T approaches zero $\Delta S = 0$, and this conclusion led Planck to
propose that for pure solids at absolute zero the entropy may become zero.

With this reference standard set up it is possible to evaluate the so-called
absolute entropies of substances. These are effectively the differences in
entropy between the substance at a specified temperature and at absolute

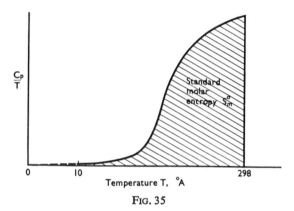

FIG. 35

zero, and are often called 'third law entropies' because of the way in which
they are obtained. Therefore we may define the *standard molar entropy* of a
substance as the difference in entropy of one mole of the substance under
'standard' conditions (25° C and one atmosphere pressure) and at absolute
zero. This is usually given the symbol S_m°.

If we are to obtain these standard molar entropies graphically, as in
Fig. 34, then we will require to know how the heat capacity of the substance
varies with temperature right down to absolute zero. Satisfactory measurements can only be made experimentally down to about 10° A, and so the
variation of the heat capacity with temperature below 10° A must either be
obtained by extrapolating the graph obtained down to that temperature,
or by employing the Debye equation which indicates that the heat capacity
is proportional to the cube of the absolute temperature at such low temperatures, i.e. $C_p = aT^3$, where a is a constant for the particular substance.
The contribution of the entropy below 10° A to the total entropy at standard
temperature is however very small, and for all purposes other than very
accurate work it can be estimated by extrapolation (see Fig. 35).

Some values of 'third law entropies' obtained in such a way have already been given in Tables 14 and 15 in Chapter 5, and Table 16 shows more values for a wider variety of substances.

TABLE 16

Gases	Cl_2	CO	CO_2	H_2O	NH_3	CH_4
S_m° e.u.	53·2	47·3	51·1	45·2	46·4	44·5

Liquids	Hg	Br_2	CH_3OH	H_2O	n-Hexane	Cyclo-hexane
S_m° e.u.	17·8	18·4	30·3	16·8	70·6	49·2

Solids	Fe	I_2	Diamond	Graphite	AgCl	AgI
S_m° e.u.	6·7	14·0	0·59	1·36	23·4	27·6

In the same way as separate heat contents should be added algebraically for the products and the reactants to determine the total heat change for a chemical reaction, so entropies can be manipulated to give entropy changes for reactions. For example, the entropy change associated with the reaction:

$$C \qquad + O_2 \quad = CO_2$$
$$\text{(graphite)} \quad \text{(g)} \qquad \text{(g)}$$

is obtained by subtracting the total entropy of the reactants from that of the products. In this case, assuming standard conditions, this would be $51·1 - (1·36 + 49·0) = +0·74$ e.u. In this case a slight increase in entropy takes place.

Evidence for the Third Law

Entropy values such as those given in Tables 14, 15 and 16, can be compared with values obtained from cell reactions or equilibrium constants (see later) which do not involve an assumption of the Third Law. In many cases the agreement is good and within the limits of experimental error. This may therefore be regarded as evidence of the reliability of the law. However, in some cases the two independent assessments do not agree with each other and this seems to indicate that some substances provide exceptions to the Third Law.

Exceptions to the Third Law

In those cases where the independent assessments differ from each other the differences are only small but they are nevertheless significant. For example, the difference between the two values for carbon monoxide is as much as one entropy unit, whereas for chlorine almost complete agreement is obtained. Again, in the case of water the difference is of the order of one entropy unit but for oxygen there is close agreement.

The accepted explanation for these observations is derived from the fact that the carbon monoxide molecule has only a small dipole moment and the two ends of the molecule are not readily distinguished from one another even though they are different. Therefore in the crystal lattice there may be some molecules lying the 'wrong way' (Fig. 36):

Because the lattice is not perfectly ordered there will be a residual entropy even at zero temperature. In the case of

```
CO  CO  CO   CO  CO

CO  CO  |OC|  CO  CO

CO  CO  CO   CO  |OC|

CO  |OC|  CO   CO  CO
```

FIG. 36

the chlorine molecule where no dipole moment exists and both ends of the molecule are identical excellent agreement can be obtained.[1]

In the case of water, where the crystal structure is the diamond type, even though each oxygen and hydrogen atom is fixed in order, the hydrogen bonds are not symmetrical, giving rise once again to a residual entropy. For oxygen, which is again symmetrical, no residual entropy is present. Thus disagreement between the two estimates of standard entropies is usually attributed to some degree of disorder in the crystal.

Summary

Entropy is a thermodynamic function, and even though it was originally defined in terms of the properties of ideal heat engines, it can be applied successfully to chemical systems. Entropy changes for chemical processes can be calculated providing that the processes are carried out reversibly, at least in theory for reversibility can never be achieved in practice. From a knowledge of the way in which the heat capacity of a substance varies with temperature the entropy difference between any two temperatures may be calculated. Absolute entropies of substances may be calculated assuming the Third Law of Thermodynamics which follows from Nernst's Heat Theorem.

The justification of the Third Law lies in the close agreement for the absolute entropies derived directly from it with those obtained by independent methods. Where there are discrepancies these can be attributed to some residual disorder in the lattice of the crystal.

[1] The maximum value of the residual entropy in the case of carbon monoxide may be simply estimated as follows. The number of different ways in which one mole of carbon monoxide can crystallise is 2^N, where N is the Avogadro number. Therefore the entropy is given by

$$S = k.\log_e 2^N = N.\frac{R}{N}\log_e 2 = R.\log_e 2 = 1\cdot38$$

7 The Measurement of Entropy Changes

We have seen how the entropy change for a given process is related to the heat absorbed or evolved and the absolute temperature T by the equation

$$\Delta S = \int \frac{dq}{T}$$

provided that the heat is absorbed or evolved in a reversible manner. Hence, one type of method which could be used for the measurement of entropy changes relies on the measurement of this heat change under reversible conditions.

Entropy of vaporisation and fusion

We have seen on page 72 how the processes of change of state are reversible ones, and therefore any method for the determination of the latent heat of vaporisation or fusion, together with an accurate measurement of the boiling-point and freezing-point respectively will furnish enough data for the calculation of the entropies of vaporisation and fusion:

$$\Delta S_v = \frac{L_v}{T_b} \quad \text{and} \quad \Delta S_f = \frac{L_f}{T_m}$$

Details of the methods for the determination of latent heats can be found in any physics textbook, and we shall not be concerned with a description here.

Entropy of transition between allotropic forms

The transformation of rhombic to monoclinic sulphur is an example of an enantiotropic change, and such a change (represented in Fig. 37) is a perfectly reversible one since equilibrium conditions are conserved throughout the transition. Thus the entropy of transition will be given by:

$$\Delta S_t = \frac{L_t}{T_t}$$

where L_t is the latent heat of transition, and T_t is the transition temperature.

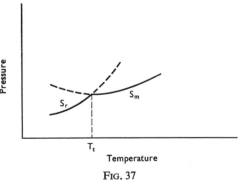

FIG. 37

In the case of sulphur the transition temperature is most easily determined by plotting a cooling curve in the normal way, and has a value of 95·6° C. The latent heat of transition is not so easily determined, but it may be done by the measurement of the variation of the vapour pressure of the sulphur with temperature, and an application of the equation

$$\log_e p = -\frac{L_t}{RT} + \text{const.}$$

where p is the vapour pressure and R the gas constant. The value for ΔS_t in this case is about 0·2 e.u.

Entropy measurements from cell reactions

Probably the most convenient method of measuring the entropy change for a chemical reaction is by arranging for the reaction to take place in an electrochemical cell. This is obviously not always possible, but in the many cases where it is the method has proved to be most satisfactory.

We have seen that when an electrochemical cell is just balanced on a potentiometer wire perfectly reversible conditions are established, for if the external e.m.f. is altered slightly in magnitude greater or less than the e.m.f. of the cell the reaction within the cell will move in the appropriate direction. Thus when balanced the cell is in a state of equilibrium, no current is flowing through it, and thermodynamically reversible conditions are established. Under such conditions, as will be shown later, the free energy change for the cell reaction is given by:

$$\Delta G = -n.E.F$$

where n is the number of electrons involved in the cell reaction, E is the e.m.f. of the cell and F is the Faraday. It can also be shown that the entropy change for the cell reaction is given by:

$$\Delta S = n.F.\left(\frac{dE}{dT}\right)$$

where dE/dT is the temperature coefficient of the cell.

Now if the reaction under investigation *can* take place in a cell and the measurements of the e.m.f. and temperature coefficient can conveniently be made, then there are two possible ways in which the entropy of the reaction can be determined.

The first of these involves only the measurement of the e.m.f. of the cell. From the equation $\Delta G = -n.E.F$ the free energy change for the reaction can be calculated. If the reaction is then allowed to proceed under irreversible conditions, for example in a calorimeter where it may go to completion, the heat change ΔH for the reaction can be estimated. Therefore by application of $\Delta G = \Delta H - T.\Delta S$ the entropy change at the temperature T at which the other measurements were taken may be calculated.

The alternative is to take measurements of the e.m.f. of the cell at different temperatures and to determine dE/dT, from which the entropy change may be obtained directly as above.

We shall now study two experiments which may be carried out in the laboratory and which illustrate the principles above.

Experiment 6
The determination of the entropy change for the reaction

$$\underset{(c)}{Zn} + \underset{(aq)}{Cu^{2+}} = \underset{(aq)}{Zn^{2+}} + \underset{(c)}{Cu}$$

The experiment is divided into two parts:

(a) the determination of ΔH,
(b) the determination of ΔG.

(a) The determination of ΔH for this reaction has already been described under Experiment 3 on page 35.
(b) The cell reaction is essentially that which takes place in the Daniell cell and such a cell may therefore be used for this experiment.

The e.m.f. of the Daniell cell may be determined by setting up the circuit shown in Fig. 38. The potentiometer wire is first of all calibrated by balancing

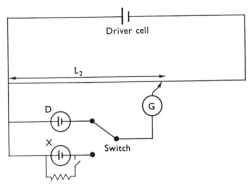

FIG. 38

the standard cell, X, when no current flows through the galvanometer G and a balance length L_1 is found on the wire. The Daniell cell, D, is then similarly balanced when a length L_2 is obtained. The standard cell usually employed for such purposes is the Weston Cadmium cell, which has an e.m.f. of 1·0183 volts at 20° C. Thus the e.m.f. of the Daniell cell is given by:

$$E = 1·0183 \times \frac{L_2}{L_1} \text{ volts}$$

The standard cell is often guarded by a high resistance while the balance is being sought, and this can be removed when a rough balance has been obtained. If a direct reading potentiometer is available the experiment will be obviously made much easier!

The free energy change will then be given by:

$$\Delta G = -n.E.F$$

where n is 2 in this case, since two electrons are transferred in the cell reaction, E is the e.m.f. measured, and F is the Faraday which can be taken as 96,000 coulombs. The value for the free energy change will thus be in units of volts-coulombs (joules) and in order to convert this to calories for comparison with ΔH the factor 0·239 is introduced. Thus the free energy change is given by:

$$\Delta G = -2 \times E \times 96{,}000 \times 0{\cdot}239 \text{ cals}$$

From the equation $\Delta G = \Delta H - T.\Delta S$ the entropy change may be calculated. The temperature T is taken as the temperature of the cell solution.

As would be expected from the species in the equation for this reaction the entropy change is quite small and therefore the utmost precaution must be taken in achieving accurate results, particularly for ΔH.

Experiment 7

The determination of the entropy change for the reaction

$$\underset{\text{(c)}}{\text{Zn}} + \underset{\text{(c)}}{\text{Hg}_2^{2+}} = \underset{\text{(aq)}}{\text{Zn}^{2+}} + \underset{\text{(l)}}{\text{2Hg}}$$

This reaction takes place in a cell as shown in Fig. 39.

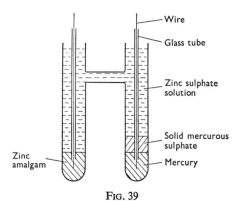

Zinc amalgam — Wire — Glass tube — Zinc sulphate solution — Solid mercurous sulphate — Mercury

Fig. 39

If such a cell is set up the e.m.f. may be measured at a known temperature in the same way as that in Experiment 6. The cell may then be transferred to a bath containing crushed ice and water, and, after allowing the system to come to thermal equilibrium, the e.m.f. may be determined once again. Intermediate temperatures may be obtained in the ice vessel by the addition

7

of warm water and several more determinations thus made. The temperature coefficient of the cell can easily be found, and the entropy change ΔS obtained from:

$$\Delta S = n.F.\left(\frac{\mathrm{d}E}{\mathrm{d}T}\right)$$

where n is equal to 2, and the result will be in joules degree^{-1} until the factor 0·239 is introduced as before.

If the temperature coefficient is negative, i.e. there is a decrease in e.m.f. as the temperature increases, the entropy change is negative, and vice versa.

An accurate potentiometer must be used for this experiment as the order of magnitude of the temperature coefficient is often between 10^{-3} and 10^{-4} volt degree^{-1}.

Part Four

Free Energy Changes in Chemical Reactions

8 Free Energy as a Thermodynamic Function

We saw in Chapter 1 how the concept of free energy became necessary in order to predict the possibility of spontaneous reaction between different substances. We saw also that since ΔH measures the change in *total* energy during the reaction, and $T\Delta S$ measures the change in energy resulting from the rearrangement of the atoms which is unavailable outside the system, then ΔG measures the energy which *is* available to do work outside the system. We noted at that point that the maximum work could only be obtained from a system when the changes were carried out reversibly, and it is this point that we shall now examine in more detail.

Free energy and net work

Most of the reactions which take place in the chemistry laboratory do so under conditions of constant temperature and pressure. Therefore, in order to simplify matters any treatment which is considered will be confined to these limitations.

We have seen in a qualitative way how the free energy change is a measure of the net work which is available outside the system. Now for an isothermal process which takes place under reversible conditions the work done by the system is a maximum. This can be shown as follows.

When one mole of an ideal gas is allowed to expand reversibly, the work done by the gas for a small increase in volume dV when the pressure of the gas (and therefore of the atmosphere outside since reversibility is established) is P is given by $P.dV$. The total work done during an expansion from a volume V_1 to V_2 will therefore be given by:

$$\text{total work done} = \int_{V_1}^{V_2} P.dV$$

Since the gas is ideal $PV = RT$ and therefore $P = \dfrac{RT}{V}$

$$\text{Thus the work done} = \int_{V_1}^{V_2} \frac{RT}{V}.dV = RT.\log_e \frac{V_2}{V_1} = RT.\log_e \frac{P_1}{P_2}$$

From the last equation it can be seen that the work done is dependent on the ratio of the initial and final gas pressures. The only way in which the work done could be increased would be by an increase in the external pressure. However, since the process is a reversible one we require the external pressure to be infinitesimally less than the gas pressure throughout the process, and if the external pressure increases by a finite amount the expansion no longer becomes possible. Hence the work done during an isothermal reversible expansion is the maximum possible.

Thus as defined by the equation $\Delta G = \Delta H - T.\Delta S$ the free energy change represents the maximum work that can be obtained from a chemical reaction other than the work of expansion, which has been allowed for in the ΔH term. Therefore the free energy measures the *useful* work that can be obtained.

If we would measure this work we must do so under reversible conditions because of what has already been said. If we attempt to carry out a measurement under irreversible conditions then the useful work obtained will not be the maximum, i.e. it will not be the free energy change. This can be seen in the Daniell cell reaction, as illustrated in Fig. 40 below.

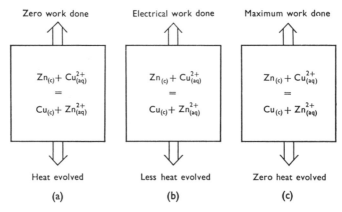

FIG. 40.   (a) Completely irreversible; (b) irreversible; (c) completely reversible.

In Fig. 40(a) the reaction is carried out in a completely irreversible manner, for example in a calorimeter. Here no useful work is obtained at all but there is an evolution of heat corresponding to the change in heat content ΔH of the reaction. In Fig. 40(b) the reaction is allowed to take place in a cell and to provide current in an external circuit. Here some useful work is obtained but at the same time some heat is evolved to the surroundings, and so the work obtained is not the maximum. Therefore the potential difference across the terminals of such a cell is less than the e.m.f. However, in Fig. 40(c) the reaction takes place in a cell and the potential difference across the terminals is balanced in a potentiometer circuit. Under such reversible conditions where no current is flowing through the cell, the electrical work done will be a maximum and there will be no wastage of energy as heat. The potential difference across the terminals under these conditions will be the e.m.f. of the cell, and since two electrons are transferred per atom of copper formed the electrical energy produced by the cell will be $2 \times E \times F$ joules, where E is the e.m.f. of the cell and F is the Faraday. In general for a reaction involving n electrons the maximum work done, and therefore the free energy of the reaction is given by $n \times E \times F$ joules. Use has already been made of this relationship in the measurement of free energy and entropy changes.

It is important to realise that whether the reaction is carried out reversibly or not the change in free energy is always the same, it is only the manifestation of this energy as useful work or as heat which varies.

It will also be obvious that ΔG can either be greater or less than ΔH, depending on the sign of the entropy change. Thus for those cells which have a positive temperature coefficient, that is an increase in entropy, there will be an absorption of heat from the surroundings when the cell is in operation and the work obtained under reversible conditions will be greater than the heat of the reaction. In some cases it may be that the free energy change and the heat change are very nearly equal. This was so with the Daniell cell reaction in Experiment 6, and in this case the change in entropy is very small.

Standard free energy changes

Since ΔH and ΔS are thermodynamic functions, and are related to the free energy change by the equation $\Delta G = \Delta H - T.\Delta S$ then ΔG too will be a thermodynamic function and will be subject to the same laws. Since ΔG is an energy change then its value will be independent of the path of the reaction (i.e. whether it is reversible or irreversible as indicated above) and will only depend on the initial and final states of the system. Thus the treatment of free energy changes is analogous to that of heat changes, as will be apparent in what follows.

Having defined the Standard Heat Change (page 16) we may therefore define the Standard Free Energy Change for a given reaction as the change in free energy which takes place when the reactants and products are in the mole quantities as indicated in the equation for the reaction, all substances being at 25° C and one atmosphere pressure. This is usually designated as $\Delta G°$.

In the same way we may define a Standard Free Energy of Formation, $\Delta G_f°$, as the free energy change taking place when one mole of the substance is formed from its elements at 25° C and one atmosphere pressure. It follows from this definition that the free energies of formation of the elements has no meaning, and it is conventional to assign zero free energy to all the elements in their standard states. The units of free energy change are the same as heat change, i.e. kcal mole^{-1}. Thus the reaction:

$$C \quad + 2H_2 \quad = CH_4$$
$$\text{(graphite)} \quad \text{(g)} \quad \text{(g)}$$

has $\Delta G_f° = -12 \cdot 0$ kcal, and the reaction:

$$2C \quad + H_2 \quad = C_2H_2$$
$$\text{(graphite)} \quad \text{(g)} \quad \text{(g)}$$

has $\Delta G_f° = +50 \cdot 0$ kcal.

The values of the free energies of formation of some common substances are given in Table 17.

TABLE 17

Solids		NaCl	AgCl	AgI	PbO	PbCl$_2$	CaCO$_3$
	ΔG_f°	$-91{\cdot}7$	$-26{\cdot}2$	$-15{\cdot}8$	$-45{\cdot}0$	$-75{\cdot}0$	-207

Liquids		C$_2$H$_6$	CH$_3$OH	C$_2$H$_5$OH	H$_2$O	H.COOH	CH$_3$COOH
	ΔG_f°	$+29{\cdot}4$	$-44{\cdot}2$	$-40{\cdot}2$	$-56{\cdot}7$	$-86{\cdot}4$	$-94{\cdot}5$

Gases		CO	CO$_2$	C$_2$H$_4$	C$_2$H$_6$	NH$_3$	H$_2$O
	ΔG_f°	$-32{\cdot}8$	$-94{\cdot}2$	$+16{\cdot}3$	$-7{\cdot}8$	$-3{\cdot}9$	$-54{\cdot}6$

In the same way as heats of formation were used with Hess's Law to determine the heat change associated with a given reaction, so too free energies of formation can be used to determine free energy changes. An example should make this clear.

Example

The standard free energies of formation of acetylene and liquid benzene are $+50{\cdot}0$ and $+29{\cdot}4$ kcal mole^{-1} respectively. Determine the free energy change, under standard conditions, for the reaction:

$$3C_2H_2 \underset{(g)}{} = \underset{(l)}{C_6H_6}$$

The free energy change for this reaction will be quite simply

$$+29{\cdot}4-(+3\times 50)\ \text{kcal} = +29{\cdot}4-150 = -120{\cdot}6\ \text{kcal}$$

Another example which includes a mixture of elements and compounds follows.

Example

The standard free energies of ethylene and ethane are $+16{\cdot}3$ and $-7{\cdot}8$ kcal respectively; determine the free energy change of the reaction:

$$\underset{(g)}{C_2H_4} + \underset{(g)}{H_2} = \underset{(g)}{C_2H_6}$$

Since the free energy of hydrogen is zero conventionally, the total change in free energy will be:

$$-7{\cdot}8-(+16{\cdot}3+0)$$
$$= -7{\cdot}8-16{\cdot}3$$
$$= -24{\cdot}1\ \text{kcal}$$

Thus the free energy change for the reaction at 25° C and all gases at one atmosphere pressure is −24·1 kcal.

The effect of temperature on the free energy change

So far we have only discussed standard free energy changes, that is those taking place at 25° C. However conditions cannot always be arranged so that a reaction can take place under exactly standard conditions, and therefore we must attempt to describe how ΔG will vary with temperature.

Because we adopted the convention of choosing the free energies of all the elements in their standard states to be zero, we found it possible to assign arbitrary free energy values to the compounds in Table 17, and we added these algebraically in order to determine the overall free energy change for the particular reaction.

Therefore before we examine the variation with temperature of the free energy change, we shall examine the variation of the free energy of a given substance.

We have already seen how the heat content and entropy of a substance vary with temperature (pages 28 and 63 respectively). Thus the heat content of a substance at a temperature T_x is given by

$$H = H_0 + \int_0^{T_x} C_p \,.\, dT + L_f + L_v$$

and the entropy of the same substance at T_x is given by

$$S = \int_0^{T_x} \frac{C_p}{T} \,.\, dT + \frac{L_f}{T_m} + \frac{L_v}{T_b}$$

Now since $G = H - TS$ the free energy of the substance at temperature T_x will be given by

$$G = H_0 + \int_0^{T_x} C_p \,.\, dT + L_f + L_v - T_x \left(\int_0^{T_x} \frac{C_p}{T} \,.\, dT + \frac{L_f}{T_m} + \frac{L_v}{T_b} \right)$$

$$G = H_0 + \int_0^{T_x} C_p \,.\, dT - T_x \int_0^{T_x} \frac{C_p}{T} \,.\, dT + \left(1 - \frac{T_x}{T_m} \right) . L_f + \left(1 - \frac{T_x}{T_b} \right) L_v$$

The coefficients of L_f and L_v are both negative since T_x is greater than either T_m or T_b, and the free energy will therefore decrease with increasing temperature, as shown in Fig. 41. There are still discontinuities at the freezing- and boiling-points but they are quite different from those on the corresponding heat content and entropy graphs.

Probably more interesting, and certainly more relevant to the present problem, is the variation of the *change* in free energy with temperature for a chemical reaction. Unless great accuracy is required it is generally permitted to assume that both ΔH and ΔS vary so slowly with temperature that they

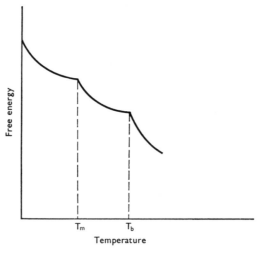

FIG. 41

may be considered to be constant, especially over limited temperature ranges. This being so, it is fairly easy to predict from the equation $\Delta G = \Delta H - T.\Delta S$ that a graph of ΔG against T will be linear, with a slope

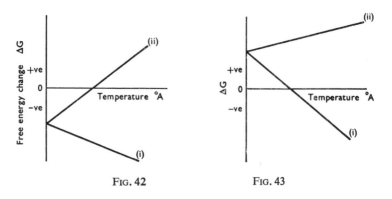

FIG. 42   FIG. 43

of ΔS and an intercept of ΔH. For a positive entropy change the graph will take the form of (i) in Fig. 42, whilst for a negative entropy change it will take the form (ii). Figure 42 represents an exothermic reaction, whilst Fig. 43 represents an endothermic reaction.

Note also that when T is zero ΔG equals ΔH. Since we have decided that spontaneous reaction will occur if ΔG is negative, it can be seen that even if the reaction is endothermic (Fig. 43) it will become thermodynamically possible provided the temperature is high enough and there is an increase in entropy, for slope (i) must cross the zero line at some temperature. In a similar way, from Fig. 43(ii) it can be seen that endothermic reactions which would have a decrease of entropy are unlikely to take place at all. Similar deductions can be made from Fig. 42, and the student should test his understanding of the principles involved with a similar treatment of this figure.

Use can be made of such graphs in the prediction of reaction between different species. A well-known example of this is the use of carbon in the

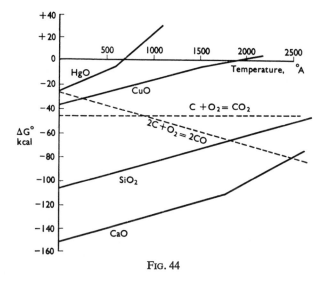

Fig. 44

reduction of metallic oxides. Figure 44 shows the variation of $\Delta G°$ (per gram atom of oxygen) with temperature of the reaction between the element concerned and oxygen to form the oxide.

From the general shape of the graphs for the oxides of the elements shown it will be appreciated that the formation of the oxide from the element and oxygen is an exothermic reaction (as would be expected from bond energies) and takes place with a decrease in entropy (since a solid and a gas are converted to a solid only). Now the more negative the free energy change for the formation of the oxide the more difficult it will be to reduce the oxide back to the metal. Thus the curves in Fig. 44 really represent the affinity which each of the elements have for oxygen, and therefore when the graph for one element lies below a second one the first element is capable (in a thermodynamic sense at least) of reducing the oxide of the second element. Thus from the graphs shown, carbon will reduce copper oxide and mercuric oxide to the metals with the evolution of CO_2 at low temperatures but CO at higher temperatures (greater than about 1,000° A), but it will not reduce silica at ordinary temperatures. At about 1,800° A the reduction of silica becomes possible, whilst the reduction of calcium oxide only becomes possible at 2,500° A. Thus silicon and calcium can be used as effective reducing agents for other metal oxides. Note that if the temperature is high enough carbon should theoretically reduce all metal oxides, since the formation of CO is accompanied by an increase in entropy, two moles of gas being formed from one. i.e.

$$\begin{array}{ccc} 2C & +O_2 & = 2CO \\ \text{(graphite)} & \text{(g)} & \text{(g)} \end{array}$$

Before the discussion on the form of Fig. 44 is ended it is worth noting the change in slope which occurs for many of the metal oxides. This obviously corresponds to a further decrease in entropy, and this arises because at a sufficiently high temperature the metal will melt, and eventually boil so that the formation of the solid oxide from the metal *vapour* and oxygen will be accompanied by a much greater decrease in entropy. Thus in the case of calcium this happens at 1773° A, the boiling-point, and for mercury at about 630° A. Since melting produces only a small change in entropy its effect on the curve will be slight, as will be the effect of a change in structure when enantiomorphism is present.

The variation of free energy change with temperature may be expressed more mathematically in the so-called Gibbs–Helmholtz equation:

$$\frac{d(\Delta G)}{dT} = \frac{\Delta G - \Delta H}{T}$$

or,

$$\frac{d(\Delta G)}{dT} = -\Delta S$$

This equation implies that if the change in heat content of a reaction is known, together with a value for ΔG at a given temperature, it is possible to calculate the value of ΔG at another temperature. Alternatively, if the rate of change of free energy with temperature is assumed to be constant, over a small temperature range, then a knowledge of ΔS will give this rate of change directly. The Gibbs–Helmholtz equation holds for constant pressure conditions. An example on the use of this equation will be given.

Example

The standard heat of formation of water is $-68\cdot3$ kcal mole^{-1} and the standard free energy of formation is $-56\cdot7$ kcal mole^{-1}. Determine the free energy of formation of water at 35° C.

Now since: $\Delta G° = \Delta H° - T.\Delta S°$

we have $-56\cdot7 = -68\cdot3 - (298 \times \Delta S°)$

Therefore

$$\Delta S° = -\frac{(68\cdot3 - 56\cdot7)}{298}$$

$$= -\frac{11\cdot6}{298}$$

$$= -0\cdot039 \text{ kcal degree}^{-1}$$

Since

$$\frac{d(\Delta G)}{dT} = -\Delta S$$

$$= +0\cdot039 \text{ kcal degree}^{-1}$$

Assuming that the rate of change of ΔG remains constant from 25° C to 35° C, we have

$$\Delta G = \Delta H + T\cdot\frac{d(\Delta G)}{dT}$$

$$= -68\cdot3 + (308 \times 0\cdot039)$$

$$= -68\cdot3 + 12\cdot0$$

$$= -56\cdot3 \text{ kcal mole}^{-1}$$

Hence the free energy of formation of water at 35° C is $-56\cdot3$ kcal mole^{-1}.

Summary

The free energy change not only indicates whether a given reaction or process will be spontaneous or not, but it also gives a measure of how much useful work the reaction is capable of doing, other than work in expansion. This work is a maximum only when the change is carried out in a perfectly reversible way, the maximum work being identical to the free energy change. The free energy change is a thermodynamic function just as heat energy and entropy are, and it can therefore be treated in a similar way. The variation of free energy and change in free energy with temperature when expressed graphically leads to a useful method of predicting spontaneous reaction, and it is expressed mathematically in the Gibbs–Helmholtz equation.

9 Free Energy and Equilibrium

We have seen how a knowledge of the sign and magnitude of the free energy change of a chemical reaction allows a prediction of its spontaneity and also of the useful work that could possibly be extracted from it. So far we have considered only reactions which are observed to proceed to any appreciable extent in one direction only. Let us now examine the free energy changes which take place for the so-called 'reversible' reactions.

Reversible reactions

It is important at the outset to distinguish between 'reversibility' in a thermodynamic sense as already explained (page 69), and 'reversibility' as applied to a chemical reaction. In the former definition we saw that the term applied to a special way of carrying out a process such that the system was at all times in perfect equilibrium with its surroundings. When applied to a chemical reaction the term 'reversible' indicates that a given reaction can proceed in either direction simultaneously, so that a dynamic equilibrium is set up; that is, when equilibrium has been achieved both the forward and back reactions are taking place simultaneously at the same rate. Probably the most familiar example of such a reaction is that between nitrogen and hydrogen to form ammonia

$$N_2 + 3H_2 \rightleftharpoons 2NH_3$$
$$\text{(g)} \qquad \text{(g)} \qquad \text{(g)}$$

In such a case we may therefore deduce that under the conditions for equilibrium both the forward and back reactions take place spontaneously. This implies that both reactions should proceed with a decrease in free

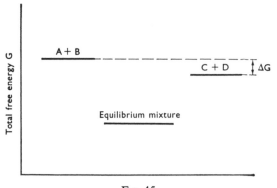

FIG. 45

energy, which seems impossible since one is the reverse of the other. The conclusion we thus arrive at is that at equilibrium the total free energy of the system is a minimum, for if it were not the system would spontaneously change to a configuration of lower free energy. We can therefore conclude that the criterion for equilibrium is that *the change in free energy is zero*, i.e. $\Delta G = 0$. This can be illustrated in Fig. 45.

In Fig. 45 the equilibrium $A + B \rightleftharpoons C + D$ is illustrated. The total free energy of the 'reactants' A and B is greater than the total free energy of the 'products' C and D. ΔG measures the free energy change for the forward reaction. Now an equilibrium mixture of A, B, C and D has a total free energy which is less than either $A + B$, or $C + D$. Hence the equilibrium mixture is in a free energy trough, and has a minimum value of free energy of all the possible arrangements. Therefore any change *from* equilibrium would involve an increase in free energy, which makes the process thermodynamically unlikely.

Free energy and the equilibrium constant

Because free energy is an extensive property its value for a given substance will depend on the concentration of the substance, and when we defined the standard free energy we therefore not only stipulated a standard temperature but also a standard concentration, i.e. in the case of a gas one atmosphere pressure. Now if the concentration varies from the standard the free energy will consequently vary also, and this will take the form

$$G = G^\circ + RT\log_e a$$

where G is the molar free energy of a substance at temperature T, when the activity of the substance is a, G° being the molar standard free energy.

Now the free energy change ΔG associated with the forward reaction of the equilibrium

$$aA + bB \rightleftharpoons cC + dD$$

will be given by:

$$\Delta G = cG_C + dG_D - aG_A - bG_B$$

where G_A etc. is the free energy of substance A.... Now from above, we have

$$G_A = G_A^\circ + RT\log_e a_A$$

Therefore

$$\Delta G = c(G_C^\circ + RT\log_e a_C) + d(G_D^\circ + RT\log_e a_D) - a(G_A^\circ + RT\log_e a_A)$$
$$- b(G_B^\circ + RT\log_e a_B)$$
$$= \Delta G^\circ + RT.\log_e\left(\frac{a_C^c \times a_D^d}{a_A^a \times a_B^b}\right)$$

This last equation applies quite generally to any conditions, and therefore if we choose the actual equilibrium conditions when $\Delta G = 0$, we can write

$$0 = \Delta G^\circ + RT.\log_e\left(\frac{a_C^c \times a_D^d}{a_A^a \times a_B^b}\right)$$

i.e.

$$\Delta G^\circ = -RT.\log_e\left(\frac{a_C^c \times a_D^d}{a_A^a \times a_B^b}\right)$$

Both terms on each side of the equation are constant so long as equilibrium conditions are established, and therefore

$$\left(\frac{a_C^c \times a_D^d}{a_A^a \times a_B^b}\right) = \text{constant} = K$$

where K is known as the equilibrium constant.

Therefore we can also write:

$$\Delta G^\circ = -RT.\log_e K$$

The last expression relating the change in standard molar free energy to the equilibrium constant is known as the van't Hoff Isotherm.

The equilibrium constant

The equilibrium constant K can be expressed in either of two alternative ways. When gas reactions are involved it is most convenient to express the activities of the substances concerned as partial pressures measured in atmospheres. When this is done the equilibrium constant is designated as K_p. Thus for reactions involving gases the van't Hoff Isotherm reads

$$\Delta G^\circ = -RT.\log_e K_p$$

In order that the substitution of partial pressures for activities may be valid the gases involved should strictly behave as ideal gases, but normally the error involved in applying this directly to real gases is not large.

For reactions in solution the activity may be replaced by the normal concentration, usually expressed in moles dm^{-3}, so long as the solutions concerned are dilute. If they are not it will be necessary to convert the concentration to activity by the use of the suitable activity coefficient. When concentrations are used the equilibrium constant is K_c. The relationship between K_p and K_c is $K_p = (RT)^{\Delta n}.K_c$, where Δn is the change in the number of moles from reactants to products.

Use of the isotherm

The isotherm may be used in one of two ways, depending on the data which is available for a given reaction. First of all, if it is possible to obtain an estimate of ΔG° from thermochemical measurements of ΔH° and ΔS° it then becomes possible to calculate the equilibrium constant at any temperature T. This information is often useful when the conditions under which a proposed reaction is likely to give economic yields is being considered, although it must be repeated at this point that the value of ΔG° will not provide any information about the rate at which equilibrium can be reached — an equally important economic consideration! Secondly, if the equilibrium constant can be measured directly in the laboratory then the value of ΔG° at any temperature can be calculated. Examples of both of these uses will be given.

Example

The standard electrode potential for the Daniell cell reaction

$$\underset{\text{(c)}}{\text{Zn}} + \underset{\text{(aq)}}{\text{Cu}^{2+}} = \underset{\text{(aq)}}{\text{Zn}^{2+}} + \underset{\text{(c)}}{\text{Cu}}$$

is 1·10 volts at 25° C. Determine the equilibrium constant for the reaction at the same temperature.

Now $\qquad \Delta G° = -n.E°.F$

Therefore $\qquad \Delta G° = -2 \times 1·1 \times 96·000$ joules

$\qquad\qquad\qquad = -211,200$ joules

$\qquad\qquad\qquad = -50,600$ cal

Since $\qquad \Delta G° = -RT.\log_e K$

$\qquad -50,600 = -2 \times 298 \log_e K$

$\qquad\qquad\qquad = -596 \times 2·303 \log_{10} K$

Therefore $\qquad \log_{10} K = \dfrac{50,600}{596 \times 2·303}$

$\qquad\qquad\qquad = 36·80$

Therefore $\qquad K = 9·03 \times 10^{36}$

In this case it is clear that the position of equilibrium lies well over to the right-hand side, i.e. the reaction is virtually complete. It will be obvious that if the equilibrium constant is less than unity then $\Delta G°$ will be positive and the position of equilibrium will lie over to the right, and vice versa.

Example

At 60° C dinitrogen tetroxide is fifty per cent dissociated. Calculate the standard free energy change at this temperature, for a pressure of one atmosphere.

$$\underset{\text{(g)}}{\text{N}_2\text{O}_4} = \underset{\text{(g)}}{2\text{NO}_2}$$

If the N_2O_4 is fifty per cent dissociated, the mole fraction of both substances is given by:

$$N_2O_4 = \frac{1-0·5}{1+0·5}; \qquad NO_2 = \frac{2 \times 0·5}{1+0·5}$$

If the total pressure is one atmosphere, the partial pressures of each are

$$p_{N_2O_4} = \frac{0·5}{1·5} \times 1 \text{ atm}$$

$$p_{NO_2} = \frac{1}{1·5} \times 1 \text{ atm}$$

The equilibrium constant K_p is given by:

$$K_p = \frac{(p_{NO_2})^2}{p_{N_2O_4}}$$

Therefore

$$K_p = \frac{1\cdot5}{(1\cdot5)^2(0\cdot5)}$$

$$= 1\cdot33 \text{ atm}$$

Since

$$\Delta G° = -RT\log_e K_p$$

We have

$$\Delta G° = -2 \times 333 \times 2\cdot303 \times 0\cdot1239$$

$$= -190\cdot0 \text{ cal}$$

Variation of equilibrium constant with temperature

The combination of the Gibbs–Helmholtz equation and the van't Hoff Isotherm leads to an equation, known as the van't Hoff Isochore, which describes the effect of temperature on the equilibrium constant.

Rewriting the Gibbs–Helmholtz equation in a more convenient form; and substituting standard conditions:

$$\Delta G° = \Delta H° + T.\frac{d(\Delta G°)}{dT} \tag{1}$$

From the van't Hoff Isotherm we have

$$\Delta G° = -RT.\log_e K_p$$

Differentiating with respect to temperature

$$\frac{d(\Delta G°)}{dT} = -R.\log_e K_p - RT.\frac{d(\log_e K_p)}{dT}$$

Therefore

$$T.\frac{d(\Delta G°)}{dT} = -RT.\log_e K_p - RT^2.\frac{d(\log_e K_p)}{dT}$$

$$= \Delta G° - RT^2.\frac{d(\log_e K_p)}{dT} \tag{2}$$

Putting (1) in (2)

$$-\Delta H° = -RT^2.\frac{d(\log_e K_p)}{dT}$$

or,

$$\frac{d(\log_e K_p)}{dT} = \frac{\Delta H°}{RT^2}$$

In the integrated form this becomes

$$\log_e K_p = -\frac{\Delta H°}{RT} + \text{constant}$$

This is one form of the van't Hoff Isochore. Perhaps a more convenient form is the one which enables a direct comparison of the equilibrium constant at two different temperatures T_1 and T_2, which is

$$\log_e\left[\frac{(K_p)_1}{(K_p)_2}\right] = -\frac{\Delta H°}{R}\left(\frac{1}{T_1}-\frac{1}{T_2}\right)$$

Le Chatelier's Principle

From inspection of the integrated form of the van't Hoff Isochore above it can be seen that if $\Delta H°$ is negative (exothermic reaction) then as T is increased K_p will decrease. Similarly, if $\Delta H°$ is positive (endothermic reaction) then K_p will increase with increasing temperature. These predictions are in accordance with Le Chatelier's Principle (1885) which states that 'if a system in dynamic equilibrium is subjected to a constraint, that change will take place in the system which will tend to remove the constraint'. Therefore for an exothermic reaction increase of temperature will favour the back rather than the forward reaction, and the position of equilibrium will move to the left.

In the integration of the van't Hoff equation above it was assumed that $\Delta H°$ was independent of temperature, which, as we have already seen, may be taken as justified over a small range of temperature. If the temperature range is large then an allowance for the variation of $\Delta H°$ with temperature must be made via the Kirchhoff equation.

If the variation of the equilibrium constant in terms of concentrations K_c is studied, then the heat change involved in the van't Hoff equation must be that at constant volume, i.e. $\Delta U°$. Thus

$$\log_e K_c = -\frac{\Delta U°}{RT}+\text{constant}$$

Summary

ΔG effectively measures how far a given reaction lies from a position of equilibrium. If the value of ΔG is large and negative then the reaction is far from equilibrium and spontaneous change towards achieving it would be predicted. If ΔG is fairly small and either positive or negative then the reaction does not lie very far from equilibrium, and when $\Delta G=0$ the position of equilibrium has been attained. Thus we see the role of the free energy change in the prediction of the extent to which a reaction is likely to go under given conditions. Even though the drive to minimum energy and to maximum entropy may oppose each other in their influence on the direction of spontaneous reaction, the sole criterion for equilibrium in a closed system remains $\Delta G=0$. The change in free energy may be related mathematically to the equilibrium constant by the van't Hoff Isotherm, and the knowledge of either of these quantities leads to an evaluation of the other. The variation of the equilibrium constant with temperature is expressed in the van't Hoff Isochore, which reinforces in a quantitative way the qualitative predictions made from Le Chatelier's Principle.

10 Summary of the Main Principles

We have noted many of the uses to which a knowledge of the free energy change can be put, and as a summary to the monograph it is now proposed that these should be classified, and clarified by the use of examples.

We may classify the use of a knowledge of ΔG for a reaction as follows:

1. To determine the direction of spontaneous change.

2. To determine the extent to which reaction takes place if it is spontaneous, i.e. the position of equilibrium.

3. To determine how much useful work can be obtained from the reaction, under suitable conditions, e.g. in a cell.

Also, if we can calculate the actual free energy of a substance, we can use this

4. To determine the stability (in a thermodynamic sense) of the substance.

Examples of each of these uses will be given.

1. Direction of spontaneous reaction

Determine whether the reaction

$$N_2 + 3H_2 = 2NH_3$$
$$\text{(g)} \quad \text{(g)} \quad \text{(g)}$$

will be spontaneous under standard conditions, i.e. 25° C and one atmosphere pressure.

First of all in a qualitative manner, we may estimate at least the sign of the changes in heat content and entropy for this reaction. So far as ΔH is concerned one strong N≡N bond and three H—H bonds are being broken but six N—H bonds are being formed. All are covalent bonds the nitrogen and hydrogen being purely covalent, while the N—H bond although probably lower in bond energy has a certain degree of polarity tending to strengthen the bond. Hence we should expect that the change in heat content for this reaction would not be very large, and would possibly be negative; i.e. the reaction will be exothermic. Taking the values of the bond energies from Tables 8 and 9 we see that the heat change for the reaction will be $(225 + 3 \times 104) - (6 \times 93 \cdot 4) = 537 - 560 \cdot 4 = -23 \cdot 4$ kcal. That is, the reaction *is* exothermic to the value of 23·4 kcal.

The entropy change is easier to estimate, at least in a qualitative way, for we see that four moles of gas are reduced to two moles during the reaction. This can only mean a decrease in entropy. From the values given in Tables 14 and 16 the entropy change is given by

$$(2 \times 46 \cdot 4) - (45 \cdot 8 + 3 \times 31 \cdot 2) = 92 \cdot 8 - 139 \cdot 4 = -46 \cdot 6 \text{ e.u.}$$

Now since $\Delta H° = -23 \cdot 4$ kcal and $\Delta S° = -46 \cdot 6$ e.u. applying $\Delta G° = \Delta H° - T\Delta S°$ we have

$$\Delta G° = -23 \cdot 4 - 298 \frac{(-46 \cdot 6)}{1,000}$$
$$= -23 \cdot 4 + 13 \cdot 9 \text{ kcal}$$
$$= -9 \cdot 5 \text{ kcal}$$

Thus at 25° C the reaction would be spontaneous since it is accompanied by a decrease in free energy. Assuming that $\Delta H°$ does not vary with temperature it is obvious that at some temperature T the change in free energy will be zero, i.e. $\Delta H° = T\Delta S°$. Above this temperature the reaction will not be spontaneous, and therefore if the reaction is to be used commercially, as it is in the Haber process, then low temperature will favour larger yields of ammonia (see 2 below).

The temperature at which $\Delta G° = 0$ is given by:

$$T.\Delta S° = \Delta H°$$

$$T = \frac{23 \cdot 4 \times 1,000}{46 \cdot 6} \quad °A$$

$$= \text{approx. } 500° A$$

It must be stressed that this temperature is a very approximate one since the constancy of $\Delta H°$ and $\Delta S°$ is not valid. However this temperature represents the region in which equilibrium between all three substances will be set up.

2. Position of equilibrium

Determine the equilibrium constant at 25° C for the reaction in (1), viz.

$$\underset{\text{(g)}}{N_2} + \underset{\text{(g)}}{3H_2} = \underset{\text{(g)}}{2NH_3}$$

We know from (1) that $\Delta G° = -9 \cdot 5$ kcal. Applying the van't Hoff Isotherm we have

$$\Delta G° = -RT.\log_e K_p$$

i.e.

$$\log_e K_p = -\frac{\Delta G°}{RT}$$

$$= \frac{9,500}{2 \times 298}$$

$$= 15 \cdot 95$$

Therefore

$$\log_{10} K_p = \frac{15 \cdot 95}{2 \cdot 303} = 6 \cdot 935$$

Therefore

$$K_p = 8 \cdot 61 \times 10^6 \text{ atm}^{-2}$$

From the value of K_p it can be seen that even at room temperature the equilibrium lies fairly well over to the right-hand side. Of course, it may be that at this temperature the rate of attainment of equilibrium is so slow that a catalyst must be employed to make the process economically possible.

3. Useful work obtainable from a reaction

The most convenient way in which the useful work obtainable from a chemical reaction can be measured is to allow the reaction to take place in a cell, and then to measure the e.m.f. of the cell with a potentiometer. Thus the work which can be obtained from the reaction

$$\underset{(c)}{Zn} + \underset{(aq)}{2Ag^+} = \underset{(c)}{2Ag} + \underset{(aq)}{Zn^{2+}}$$

can be found by setting up the standard cell

$$Zn|Zn^{2+}(1 \text{ gm. ion } dm^{-3})|Ag^+(1 \text{ gm. ion } dm^{-3})|Ag$$

The standard e.m.f. of such a cell is found to be 1·56 volts. Now when the cell is working under reversible conditions the maximum useful work is given, and this equals the change in free energy,

i.e.
$$\Delta G^\circ = -n.E^\circ.F$$
$$= -2 \times 1 \cdot 56 \times 96,500 \text{ joules}$$
$$= -72 \text{ kcal}$$

The fuel cell

An example of the way in which the free energy change for a chemical reaction can be utilised in doing work is seen in the recent development of the fuel cell. In one such cell hydrogen is supplied to one electrode (negative) and oxygen to the other one, the electrolyte being potassium hydroxide solution. The hydrogen gas is effectively burned as a fuel according to the equation:

$$\underset{(g)}{H_2} + \underset{(g)}{\tfrac{1}{2}O_2} = \underset{(l)}{H_2O}$$

for which the free energy change for the mole reacting quantities shown is −56·7 kcal. Thus the e.m.f. of such an arrangement is about 1·23 volts and it is capable of supplying currents up to 5 amps in some of the designs on the market. The cells are highly efficient and will become increasingly important as a means of conversion of chemical energy to electrical energy.

4. Determination of the stability of a substance

One of the most interesting uses to which ΔG values can be put is in helping to decide whether a proposed compound is likely to be stable or not. For example, it is proposed that nitrogen may polymerise, under suitable conditions, to a cyclic nitrogen compound analogous to the polymerisation of acetylene to benzene,

$$3N_2 = N \overset{\displaystyle N-N}{\underset{\displaystyle N=N}{\Big\langle\ \ \ \Big\rangle} N}$$

In order to determine whether such a reaction is likely or not we can either calculate what the free energy change for the reaction is likely to be, or attempt to calculate the actual free energy of the compound itself. We can estimate the free energy change for the proposed reaction as follows.

The change in heat content for the reaction will derive from the breaking of three pi bonds in nitrogen and the reforming of three N—N bonds. Each pi bond requires approximately 70 kcal to rupture and each single N—N bond liberates 56 kcal (values per mole of bonds), and therefore the reaction as proposed would be endothermic by at least 42 kcal. Allowance must be made for a resonance effect in the cyclohexazide ring, let us assign the same value as for benzene, e.g. about 40 kcal. This means that ΔH would either be zero or very slightly positive.

So far as the entropy change is concerned, if the cyclohexazide is formed in the vapour state, there will still be a substantial decrease in entropy, since the ring structure is by far the more organised one.

Therefore we must predict a positive value for ΔH and a negative value for ΔS, which can only lead to a positive value for ΔG. This means that the reaction as written is unlikely to proceed, indeed the reverse reaction is much more probable, and the cyclic compound is therefore likely to be unstable.

Further Reading

MOTT-SMITH, MORTON. *The Concept of Energy Simply Explained*, Dover Publications Inc., New York. An elementary, non-technical account of energy traced from its beginnings through the important period of the nineteenth century to the present day. Also included are short biographies of some of the men who contributed to the discovery and development of the subject.

A more mathematical approach will be found in the following:
MOORE, WALTER J. *Physical Chemistry*, Longmans.
GLASSTONE, S. *Textbook of Physical Chemistry*, Macmillan.

Further details of experimental determinations of heat, entropy and free energy changes will be found in:
PALMER, W. G. *Experimental Physical Chemistry*, Cambridge University Press.

Index

Absolute entropy, 74
Association, 66
Average bond energy, 47

Bond dissociation energy, 47
Bond energy
  constancy, 49
  definition, 46
  tables of, 46, 49
Born-Haber cycle, 43

Calorimeter, 29
  adiabatic, 30
  bomb, 30
  constant, 31, 33
  ice, 31
Cell reaction, 79
Change in heat content, 5
Closed system, 9
Complex ion, 66
Conservation of energy, 20
Continuous variation method, 37
Coordinate bond, 55
Covalent bond, 45
Criterion for equilibrium, 94
  spontaneous reaction, 11

Diffusion of gases, 7
Disorder, 8
Dissociation, thermal, 65
Driving force, 3, 11
Dulong and Petit, 25

Endothermic reaction, 5
Energy, equipartition of, 39
  of Hydration, 44
  potential, 40
  rotational, 39
  translational, 39
  vibrational, 39
Enthalpy, 24
Entropy, 8, 70
  and probability, 61
  and temperature, 63
  change, 7

Entropy—*cont.*
  of fusion, 78
  of gases, 67
  of solids, 68
  of vaporisation, 63, 78
  tables of, 67, 68
Entropy unit, 63, 68, 71
Entropy zero, 8
Equilibrium constant, 96
Equilibrium and free energy, 94
Exothermic reaction, 5
Expansion of a gas, 69
Extensive property, 61, 69

First law of thermodynamics, 19
Free energy, 10
  and equilibrium, 94
  and temperature, 89, 90
  changes, tables of, 88
  of formation, 87
Fuel cell, 102

Gaseous state, 62
Gibbs-Helmholtz equation, 92

Heat capacity, 24
  at constant pressure, 25
  at constant volume, 25
Heat change, 15
  at constant pressure, 22
  at constant volume, 22
Heat content, 5
Heat of Combustion, 17
    table of, 17
  Dilution, 19
  Dissociation, 18
    table of, 18
  Formation, 16
    table of, 16
  Neutralisation, 18, 33
  Reaction, 16, 35
  Solution, 19, 35, 44
Hess's law, 20
Hydration of ions, 44
Hydrogen bond, 57

Infinite dilution, 19
Intensive property, 69
Internal energy, 24
Ionic bond, 40
    charge, 43
    size, 42
Irreversible change, 11
Irreversible process, 69
Isentropic change, 71
Isolated system, 7
Isotherm, van't Hoff, 96

Kinetic energy, 39
Kirchhoff's equation, 25

Latent heat of fusion, 78
    transition, 79
    vaporisation, 78
Lattice energy, 40, 42
    table of, 42
Lavoisier and Laplace, 19
Le Chatelier's principle, 99
Liquid state, 62

Madelung constant, 41
Maximum work, 85
Metallic bond, 56

Open system, 9

π bond, 53
Polarisation, 44
Polarity, 52
Polymerisation, 66
Potential energy, 40
Probability and entropy, 61

Reduction of oxides, 91
Resonance, 54
Resonance energy, 55

Reversible change, 11
Reversible process, 69, 79
Rotational energy, 39
Rubber stretching, 9

Second law of thermodynamics, 4, 71
σ bond, 53
Sign convention, 15
Solid state, 61
Solubility, 44
Spontaneous process, 4
    reaction, 3
Standard free energy change, 87
Standard heat change, 15–16
Standard molar entropy, 75

Temperature and free energy change, 89
Temperature coefficient, 79
Thermal dissociation, 65
Thermodynamics, 69
Third law entropy, 75
    table of, 76
Third law, evidence for, 76
    exceptions to, 76
Third law of thermodynamics, 74
Translational energy, 39

Units, entropy, 63, 68, 71
    heat change, 15

van der Waals force, 58
van't Hoff Isochore, 98
van't Hoff Isotherm, 96
Vapour pressure, 79
Vibrational energy, 39

Zero entropy, 8, 62
Zero-point energy, 48

DATE DUE

MAY 1 '84			
GAYLORD			PRINTED IN U.S.A.